510/

FRIENDS
OF ACPL

3 1833 00602 1069

D1171083

SAN FRANCISCO 49ers

SAN

The Coward-McCann Sports Library

FRANCISCO
49 ERS

by Dan McGuire

FULLY ILLUSTRATED

COWARD-McCANN, INC.   **NEW YORK**

j 796.332

© 1960 BY AMERICAN SPORTS PUBLISHING COMPANY, INC.

All rights reserved. This book, or parts thereof, must not be reproduced in any form without permission. Published on the same day in the Dominion of Canada by Longmans, Green & Company, Toronto.

Library of Congress Catalog Card
Number: 60-11290

MANUFACTURED IN THE UNITED STATES OF AMERICA

Contents

CO. SCHOOLS
C509423

6203453

Foreword

As Mayor of the City and County of San Francisco it is a pleasure to commend Mr. Dan McGuire for the tremendous research project undertaken in relation to the publication of this volume.

The history of San Francisco's professional football team and that of the late beloved Tony Morabito constitute a major portion of the history of athletics in this exceedingly sports-conscious community.

Since 1946 the San Francisco 49ers have represented San Francisco throughout the nation with dignity and good sportsmanship and have constantly reflected credit to this community.

I am confident that the years ahead will continue to add additional chapters to San Francisco's ever-increasing pride in its beloved professional football team.

GeoChristopher
Mayor

May 10, 1960

Red Hickey

Introduction

by *HOWARD W. (RED) HICKEY*
Head Coach
San Francisco 49ers

AFTER banquet-circuit oratory during the recent off season, I was frequently reminded by members of my captive audience that I had designated 1959 as a "building year" for the San Francisco 49ers.

And they invariably added: "What's your excuse for 1960?"

My ensuing sermon on the theory that Rome wasn't built in a day usually elicited only loud groans of anguish and despair.

Actually, the patience and forbearance of 49ers rooters are in pleasant contrast to the usual "in or else" demand in sports. For fourteen years they have hungered for a championship club. But, win or lose, they have supported their team in a manner that has made San Francisco one of the great cities of professional football.

They deserve a winner—and it's my job to get one for them.

We made a run for the top in both 1957 and 1959. In analyzing the near misses of those clubs, we would probably have to go back to the drafts of 1953 and 1954 when the 49ers failed to get their proper share of the available material. Only two men from the college drafts of those years—Bob St. Clair in 1953 and Ted Connolly a year later—became solid, lasting performers for the 49ers.

We believe we overcame this crucial weakness with the

11

appointment of Lynn (Pappy) Waldorf as our director of personnel or, in simpler words, talent scout. We had nine rookies on our roster at the end of the 1959 season; four or five of those boys can become truly great players in the National Football League.

Pappy is on the road nine months of the year. He visits all the major schools and most of the smaller ones. He watches practice sessions both in the fall and in the spring. From February through May the other members of our staff also tour the country to embellish Pappy's work.

Working directly under Pappy are more than 60 part-time scouts in every section of the nation. They begin submitting reports on a player when he is a sophomore. These reports are cross-checked so that conflicting testimony can be gone over at endless meetings.

There are approximately 700 colleges and universities participating in intercollegiate football. Before the last draft session we had complete cards on 2,000 seniors. We endeavored to limit our final list to the best 400.

You can readily see why scouting has become a $100,000 item in a pro club's budget.

As far as my own coaching philosophy is concerned, I believe I can best sum it up by saying that I expect a 100 per cent desire to win 100 per cent of the time. That desire is the distinguishing characteristic of the great player who is never satisfied with second place.

In this business your most frustrating experience is to find a player with size, speed and reflexes but sadly lacking in the all-important requirement of desire.

I think we had that spirit on our 1959 team which, on paper at least, was not figured to be among the contenders. We stayed on top until the last two weeks of the season when various factors, including a lack of bench strength, caught up with us.

If our veterans continue to display such spirit, we could have an improved team in 1960. I am also counting on the expected improvement of last year's rookies and some much-needed help from this year's newcomers.

We will have one of the most exciting players in the NFL in Ray Norton, the Olympic sprinter, generally regarded as the world's fastest human. In all honesty, I think it will take Ray at least two seasons to adapt himself to pro football. He had very little gridiron experience in college at San Jose State and will miss almost all of training camp.

With the running game again a vital factor in pro ball, Monty Stickles of Notre Dame could be a key rookie at the "tight" end position. You have to have offensive ends of Stickles' size—six feet four, 240 pounds—if you intend to get past the huge defensive linemen and linebackers in the NFL.

Other rookie linemen who carry our hopes include Jerry Hurst, Middle Tennessee; Mike Magac, Missouri; Len Rohde, Utah State, and Rod Breedlove, Maryland. Hurst was drafted in 1957 but spent two seasons in Canada. The others were prominent in collegiate circles last year.

But there is nothing as indefinite as success at a pro training camp. On occasions too numerous to mention, unknown players from small schools have won jobs from men with all kinds of All-America clippings.

In 1958, Jerry Mertens joined us from Drake as an unheralded end candidate. He was a 20th draft choice. By the time the season began he was our first-string left halfback on defense and has been one of the best in the league.

If nine rookies survive this time, we'll have had a 50 per cent turnover of personnel in two years. That would certainly bear out my "building" plans. But I've learned one thing during my career—the best coach is the one with the best players.

SAN FRANCISCO 49 ers

49er owners early in 1957. *Seated:* Victor Morabito, Tony Morabito, Dr. William E. O'Grady. *Standing:* Lawrence Purcell, Albert Ruffo, Franklin Mieuli, James Ginella.

Prologue

THE afternoon of Sunday, October 27, 1957, was cold and gloomy in San Francisco. Fog had billowed in early from the Pacific, three miles to the west of Kezar Stadium, and hung like a pall over the capacity crowd of nearly 60,000.

It wasn't the weather, however, that depressed the spirits of those crammed into the ancient bowl. They had watched in disbelief and despair as their beloved 49ers dropped two touchdowns in arrears to the aroused Chicago Bears in less than nine minutes of play.

The 49ers had won three of their four National Football League games, arousing hopes for San Francisco's first championship in eleven years of professional competition.

The almost eerie silence was broken by a florid-faced fan who jumped to his feet, turned toward the guest box, and bellowed: "Hey, Tony! Same old story—fast start, then the blowup!"

Anthony J. Morabito, founder and president of the 49ers, stared straight ahead for a moment, then looked at his younger brother and partner, Victor, and murmured: "I can't blame them for being angry and disappointed. We've got the best fans in the country and we've let them down so many times. But I've a hunch on this ball club—it won't fold."

On the field, the 49ers began to act as if they had heard the vote of confidence by their employer. Quarterback Y. A. Tittle's passes found friendly targets and the team in the cardinal jerseys drove in for its first touchdown. The stadium rocked with the traditional San Francisco chant of "Go! Go! Go!"

As the Bears lined up to receive the kickoff, Vic Morabito was surprised to note that Willie Galimore, the brilliant rookie halfback, was not in his customary receiving position. He remarked on this to his brother. Just then Galimore ran off the bench and replaced one of the safety men.

"For Pete's sake, Vic, look what you've done!" growled Tony. "The Bears heard you. It's your fault if Galimore goes all the way!"

Galimore didn't, but the Bears picked up nine yards in two rushes. It was third down and one to go.

"This is the key play," declared Tony. "If we can hold them now, we'll be back in the game."

Quarterback Ed Brown tried to roll out around his own left end and was thrown for a five-yard loss by Bill Herchman, 49er tackle.

At that moment, Tony slumped back in his seat, choking and gasping. Death, at his elbow since a near-fatal heart attack in 1952, had come to collect the final installment.

Dr. Frank Cox, sitting nearby, immediately began applying artificial respiration while Vic raced down the steps and across the field to summon Dr. Bill O'Grady, the team's and Tony's physician.

Father William McGuire gave Final Absolution and to him Tony whispered his last words: "Thank you, Father."

How the 49ers, weeping unashamedly, surged back in the second half to upset the Bears is related elsewhere in this book. For the story of the 49ers is the story of Tony Morabito. Controversial (especially as far as some newspapermen were concerned) and colorful (he would have resented the adjective), Tony received one of his highest tributes from Bill Leiser, a sports editor with whom he had disagreed.

"Tony was the man who made San Francisco a major league city," Leiser wrote in the *Chronicle*.

And this is the story of how he did it.

CHAPTER 1

"Go Get a Football"

ANTHONY J. MORABITO received a polite but firm brush-off when he first sought a National Football League franchise for San Francisco just before World War II.

The statement he heard most frequently was that transportation problems were the main stumbling block in extending schedules to the Pacific Coast.

One of the owners patted him paternally on the shoulder and said, "We've got ten clubs operating now. Only four of them have ever shown a profit. More than forty other franchises have gone broke. Stay in the lumber business—you'll be better off."

Tony was rebuffed again at the NFL meeting in 1942. This time he left behind a prediction that by the end of the war athletic teams would be able to travel almost exclusively in airplanes.

"San Francisco and Los Angeles will be only a few hours—not days—from New York," he argued. "Vote me a franchise now and I'll have it ready to operate three months after the war is over."

He heard himself described as an "impractical dreamer" and returned, discouraged, to San Francisco.

When he was growing up in the North Beach area of his native city, Tony did have football dreams. But in these flights of fancy he was always making long touchdown runs while thousands of people cheered. His schoolday chums were far more interested in baseball, for the North Beach playgrounds were the incubators for great stars such as Tony Lazzeri, Frank Crosetti, and the DiMaggio brothers.

Tony played high school football with moderate success at St. Ignatius, then enrolled at the University of Santa Clara in the fall of 1927. A few weeks later a serious shoulder injury ended his football career.

But he didn't lose his interest in the sport and often attended practice sessions as well as never missing a game. He was particularly impressed by the work of a young assistant coach, Lawrence T. (Buck) Shaw, who arrived at Santa Clara in 1929.

The worlds of commerce and industry were not waiting with open arms when Tony received his college diploma in 1931. The nation was in the throes of the Great Depression. Tony's father—an immigrant from Italy—had built up a flourishing ship's service concern on the San Francisco waterfront, only to see business dwindle to almost nothing.

Tony felt he was lucky when he got a job driving a truck for eighty dollars a month. He had a remarkable ability to get along with people in all walks of life and was a natural-born salesman. By 1940, when he was thirty years old, he was successful in the lumber carrier business.

He maintained his interest in college football, especially the fortunes of Santa Clara.

"About this time," he recalled later, "I began to hear more

about professional football. This was mainly due to the fact that Nello Falaschi, who had been the quarterback for Shaw's first Sugar Bowl team in 1936, had become a star with the New York Giants."

Soon he became almost obsessed with the desire to obtain an NFL franchise for San Francisco. His second turndown by the league was followed by another blow—the Army wouldn't take him because of his growing deafness. This affliction later forced him to full-time use of a hearing aid.

One day in 1943 he walked into the office of Bill Leiser, sports editor of the *Chronicle*. As Leiser tells the story:

"He seemed a cautious, soft-walking, soft-talking, mousy type of man. He was neither cautious nor mousy. He said he wanted to talk about the possibility of success for professional football in San Francisco. I asked him if he expected to hire a football team, start playing games and make a million. I told him it would take a long time, that he'd have to be prepared to lose a lot of money.

"He said he was well aware of that, and was prepared to lose.

"I asked him what his idea was as to a football coach.

"He said his idea was Buck Shaw, that he had already talked to Buck and believed he could sign him.

"Many men had been around to talk of pro football, but this was the first who had any idea it was necessary to lose money getting organized and selling the game in San Francisco. And the first prepared to hire a top-class coach at the outset, one who, by his own prestige, would go a long way in selling the pro game.

"Tony was prepared to hire Shaw 'right now' and start paying his salary, even though Buck certainly could not have a football team to coach until the war ended."

Impressed, Leiser told Tony that a new pro league, the All-America Conference, was being formed in secret by Arch

Ward, sports editor of the *Chicago Tribune*. And Tony was present for the organizational meeting of the AAC at St. Louis, June 4, 1944.

Teams represented, besides San Francisco, were the Cleveland Browns, Los Angeles Dons, Buffalo Bills, and Chicago Rockets. Three other clubs were added later—the Brooklyn Dodgers, New York Yankees, and Miami Seahawks.

James H. Crowley, one of Notre Dame's immortal Four Horsemen, was the AAC's first commissioner. His teammate, Elmer Layden, was commissioner of the NFL at that time.

Tony had a comfortable income, but he could hardly expect to compete with such financial titans as Ben Lindheimer at Los Angeles; Dan Topping, New York; Jim Breuil, Buffalo; and Arthur (Mickey) McBride, Cleveland. Accordingly, his partners in Lumber Terminals of San Francisco—Allen E. Sorrell and E. J. Turre—came in on the football deal. Victor Morabito also had a small interest in the project.

It was Turre who suggested the club's unique nickname. As students of United States history know, gold was discovered in California in 1848. The men who made the perilous voyage around Cape Horn and poured into the gold fields the following year became known as 49ers.

There was no formal declaration of war with the NFL, yet it wasn't long before heavy verbal barrages were fired back and forth. An official of the established league gave the AAC its rallying cry when he predicted quick defeat for the upstart circuit and added: "Tell them to go get a football!"

When Japan threw in the towel, many discharged servicemen noted for their football prowess found themselves in the delightful position of being sought by two rival leagues. In some cases, the bidding reached fantastic levels, and the AAC did quite well in signing men who had starred in the NFL before going into military service.

The 49ers struck a major blow for the new league when

they nabbed Norm Standlee, who had been an All-America fullback at Stanford and a rookie sensation with the Chicago Bears in 1941.

Other members of the first 49ers squad with previous professional experience included:

Leonard Eshmont, halfback, Fordham, New York Giants; Bruno Banducci, guard, Stanford, Philadelphia Eagles; Parker Hall, halfback, Mississippi, Cleveland Rams; Bill Fisk, end, U.S.C., Detroit Lions; Dick Bassi, guard, Santa Clara, Chicago Bears; Arthur (Dutch) Elston, center, South Carolina, Cleveland Rams; John Mellus, tackle, Villanova, New York Giants; John Woudenberg, tackle, Denver U., Pittsburgh Steelers; Gerry Conlee, center, St. Mary's, Cleveland Rams; Bob Titchenal, end, San Jose State, Washington Redskins; Bob Bryant, tackle, Texas Tech, Philadelphia Eagles.

The 49ers hit the jackpot when they signed Frankie Albert, the left-handed quarterback who had led Stanford's "Cinderella" team to an undefeated season and the Rose Bowl in 1940. It was a prestige move, not only locally but nationally.

The little southpaw, given full rein by Shaw, was to put an indelible stamp of color and excitement on the 49ers.

CHAPTER 2

The "Silver Fox" Turns Pro

PREMATURELY gray and handsome as a movie idol, Lawrence Timothy (Buck) Shaw was undoubtedly the most respected athletic figure in the San Francisco Bay Area when Tony Morabito signed him to coach the 49ers in the fledgling All-America Conference.

He had won national recognition with his Santa Clara teams, particularly the 1936 and 1937 aggregations which captured upset victories in the Sugar Bowl. It was well known in many circles that Buck had turned down an offer from Notre Dame, his alma mater, in 1941 because he preferred to live in or near San Francisco.

His acceptance of the 49er job immediately converted many of the cynics who had predicted a short and unmerry life for the new league. "If Buck says it's okay, then we're for it," was the general reaction.

Polished and urbane, a dapper dresser, he usually amazed strangers when he identified himself as a football coach. In

Buck Shaw

rare moments of displeasure his roughest language was, "Darn it to hell!" When he burst forth with that, however, many a lagging team displayed startling improvement.

Buck was born and raised on a farm near Stuart, Iowa. He enrolled at Creighton University in Omaha in the fall of 1918 and immediately began as starting tackle on the football varsity. The influenza epidemic of that year forced Creighton to abandon the schedule after only four games and Buck returned home. The following spring he registered at Notre Dame.

The Fighting Irish were unbeaten during Buck's sophomore and junior years as he spearheaded a line that opened the way for the great George Gipp. They lost only to Iowa when he was a senior.

Blessed with Knute Rockne's personal recommendation, Buck coached at North Carolina State and the University of Nevada before going to Santa Clara as assistant to Maurice (Clipper) Smith.

He was almost ready to forego football in favor of a business career when Smith surprised everyone in 1936 by resigning. Through 1942, when the school suspended football for the duration, Buck's Broncos won forty-seven games, tied four and lost only ten.

Then came the bid from Tony Morabito, and he accepted the challenge of pro football.

For his assistants he chose Albert J. (Al) Ruffo, his chief aide at Santa Clara, and James W. (Jim) Lawson, long-time member of the Stanford staff.

Ruffo, a classmate of Tony's, had been an outstanding lineman. He also excelled scholastically, gaining a master's degree in electrical engineering. Then he transferred to law and built up a thriving practice in San Jose, California, while coaching on the side.

Lawson had been an inspirational end on the Stanford

teams led by the fabled Ernie Nevers. He played profession-
ally with an all-star team organized by Red Grange and subsequently returned to Stanford as an assistant to Glenn S.
(Pop) Warner. Jim also served under Claude (Tiny) Thornhill
and Clark Shaughnessy before receiving a Navy commission
in 1942.

The success story of the 49ers, as far as players are concerned, has to begin with Frankie Albert. Some men are
born under a strange star that directs them to the right place
at the right time. Albert was one of the chosen few.

Frankie grew up in Glendale, California, where he was
always the little guy who was trying to break into teams con-
trolled by bigger, tougher and older companions. He signed
up for the football team as a sophomore at Glendale High,
but they wouldn't issue him a uniform.

"Sorry, Albert," a coach said, "you're too small. We don't
want you to get hurt."

Frank worked out on his own, determined to prove that
size wasn't everything. He realized, perhaps better than his
superiors, that there were compensating factors of desire and
intelligence. As a junior, he was the school's starting quarterback and the following year, 1937, George T. Davis, sports
editor of the Los Angeles *Herald-Express,* named him Southern California's "Prep Athlete of the Year."

Most college coaches took one look at his physical dimen-
sions—five feet eight inches, 160 pounds—and crossed him off
their scholarship lists. His enrollment at Stanford in the fall
of 1938 passed almost unnoticed.

After the "Wow Boy" era of 1933–35, which included three
consecutive Rose Bowl appearances, Stanford had fallen into
losing ways. Albert was lost in Coach Tiny Thornhill's
double-wing formation and in his sophomore year the school
had its worst football record of all time—one win, one tie and
eight defeats.

Destiny, in the form of Clark Daniel Shaughnessy, stepped in. The University of Chicago, humiliated in Big 10 competition, had dropped football and Stanford, to everyone's amazement, picked Shaughnessy, the last coach at the Midway, as Thornhill's successor.

When Shaughnessy arrived at Palo Alto in the spring of 1940, he had no idea what system he would install. Years later he told a friend: "After two spring workouts, I knew the answer—the T formation. Albert didn't have the passing arm of a Sammy Baugh or Sid Luckman but, somehow, he got the ball to the receivers. I also realized that with his great running ability he'd drive defenses crazy trying to figure whether he was going to pass or run when he rolled out of the pocket. And he was a magnificent punter.

"Then there was Norm Standlee, a 230-pound fullback who had the speed to run the ends. And a pair of quick-starting, elusive halfbacks in Hugh Gallarneau and Pete Kmetovic. For me, it was a coach's dream."

Shaughnessy, during his years in Chicago, had been an advisory coach with the Bears who, of course, had exploited the T successfully for many seasons. But the vast majority of professional and college teams used the Notre Dame system, or the single and double wings.

Under Albert's leadership, Stanford stunned the football world by rolling to nine straight victories. The Indians made Nebraska their tenth victim in the Rose Bowl, 21–13.

The impact on football, professional, college and high school, was revolutionary. Team after team shifted to the T's wide-open style. The emphasis on passing and quick openers was quickly appreciated by the paying customers.

Little wonder, then, that Albert, when he returned from wartime naval duty in the Pacific, was besieged with professional offers. With a big assist from Jim Lawson, who had

Alyn Beals and Visco Grgich

helped coach him at Stanford, Shaw and Morabito signed him for the 49ers.

There were many other players on the first 49er team in 1946 who didn't have professional experience. They had finished college in 1941 or 1942 and were in Army, Navy, Air Force or Marine Corps uniforms during or immediately after commencement exercises.

From his last Santa Clara teams, Shaw signed Alyn Beals, a brilliant pass receiver, Ken Casanega, Eddie Forrest, Rupert Thornton, and Visco Grgich, who became one of the best middle guards in pro ball. From Washington State came Nick Susoeff, Joe Remington, and Dick Renfro. Stanford also contributed Hank Norberg, while Pete Franceschi represented the University of San Francisco. Don Durdan had been a halfback on Oregon State's 1941 Rose Bowl team.

Thus, the 49ers from their very inception had a Bay Area and Pacific Coast flavor.

Special mention must be made of Johnny (Strike) Strzykalski, a carefree, fun-loving Milwaukee product who had only one goal when he tucked a football under his arm—all the way. Strike had played two years at Marquette before enlisting and was with the powerful 4th Air Force team from March Field when Tony and Buck met him in 1945.

After listening to their offer, Strike said, "Okay, I'll take it—if you'll also sign my buddy, Joe Vetrano."

The 49er officials hadn't heard of Vetrano but if Strike, who was being wooed by rival organizations, wanted him, that was it. Vetrano, the "Little Toe," became one of the finest place kickers in the game and at one time owned the all-time pro record of 107 consecutive extra points.

Frankie Albert, "coach on the field"

CHAPTER 3

The All-America Conference Begins

TONY MORABITO wasn't present when the 49ers made their professional debut by defeating the Los Angeles Dons, 17–7, in an exhibition game at San Diego's Balboa Stadium on August 25, 1946.

Tony and Vic had attended the All-Star game in Chicago and were scheduled to fly to Denver where they would board a direct flight to Los Angeles—San Diego. Arriving in Denver, they found their reservations hadn't been confirmed and they sat glumly in the terminal as the connecting plane roared down the runway without them.

Tony refused to give up.

"We'll charter a plane," he told Vic.

A few minutes later they were airborne in an open-cockpit relic that Vic swore must have been left over from the First World War.

"As soon as we took off," he recounted, "I was all for landing again. I started yelling at Tony but he ignored me. We hit a snowstorm and began bouncing all over the sky. Mountain peaks looked close enough to touch. After a while I got sick and only wished I could die."

The pilot-owner of the plane somehow found Albuquerque and landed.

"This is as far as I go," he announced. "You guys may be crazy, but I'm not."

"That's up to you," Tony said. "Now, how about a refund of our dough for the Albuquerque–San Diego part of the flight?"

The pilot's answer, as he walked away, was impolitely negative.

Several weeks later Tony wrote a letter to the pilot in Denver: "I just wanted to tell you how I enjoyed our ride to Albuquerque. It was indeed a shame we couldn't complete the trip. By the way, our football team will be making a stop in Denver next month and I'm going to bring in some of the boys to meet you."

The refund check arrived within two days.

On September 1, the 49ers appeared before a home audience at Kezar Stadium for the first time and overcame the Chicago Rockets, 34–14, in another exhibition contest. The reaction to major league pro football was heartening.

Curley Grieve, sports editor of the *Examiner,* wrote:

A throng of 45,000 thrilled spectators agreed this afternoon professional football "has something." That "something," as demonstrated by the San Francisco 49ers and Chicago Rockets, was high entertainment value, poise, power and dazzling offense.

Coach Dick Hanley of the Rockets coined a phrase that was to get much mileage: "That Frankie Albert is a coach on the field. He's easily the last word in the nation in working the T."

Things looked very bright for the first regular ACC game with the New York Yankees on September 8. Tony and Buck

The first 49er backfield: John Strzykalski, left half; Norm Standlee, fullback; Len Eshmont, left half; Frank Albert, quarterback

were both restrained in their enthusiasm, however, for they knew the Yankees were made up almost entirely of pro veterans. Most of the personnel had been with Dan Topping's Brooklyn team in the NFL before he shifted the franchise to the AAC.

C509423 CO. SCHOOLS

The fears were well founded. The heavier Yankee line manhandled the 49er forwards and rushed Albert off his feet. Orban (Spec) Sanders, a memorable name in pro ball, operated brilliantly at left halfback in Coach Ray Flaherty's single wing. The final verdict was 21 to 7.

The size of the 49er linemen that afternoon, as compared to present-day standards, is startling. The tackles, Mellus and Woudenberg, weighed 218 and 225, respectively; the guards, Bassi and Banducci, were both 215, and the center, Elston, was 190.

The average weight of the players manning the same five positions in 1959 was 252 pounds!

Less than 20,000 people showed up for the second league game as the 49ers achieved the right side of the scoreboard over the Miami Seahawks, 21–14. Brooklyn was victimized the next week, 32–13, and the club left on a five-game road trip.

If Shaw were asked to relate the most embarrassing experience of his coaching career, he'd have no trouble replying. It happened in Chicago that year. The Rocket owners had fired Coach Hanley and three players had taken over the masterminding—Bob Dove, "Wee Willie" Wilkin and Ned Mathews.

In spite of this weird arrangement, the Rockets throttled the 49ers, 24–7. The coaching fraternity all over the country reeled from the blow. This was anarchy! The panic subsided finally when Pat Boland and Ernie Nevers assumed the coaching reins of the Rockets.

The 49ers finished their inaugural season with a record of nine wins and five losses. Their most notable achievement was a 34 to 20 victory over the Cleveland Browns in the first chapter of what was to become the prime rivalry of the AAC. The 49er exchequer also got a much-needed boost from the gate receipts provided by a Cleveland crowd of more than 70,000.

The Browns won the Western Division title with a 12–2 mark and nipped the Yankees (10–3–1 in the Eastern Division) by a 14–9 count in the championship play-off.

San Francisco gained some consolation when Beals and Banducci were named on the official All-ACC team, with Albert and Standlee receiving second team honors.

Jack McDonald, sports editor of the *Call-Bulletin,* quoted Tony as saying the 49er losses for 1946 ran "just short of $150,000. But we didn't expect to make any money this year and aren't counting on a profit next season."

The Browns were the only club that operated on the black

side of the ledger. Miami folded and the other teams had to contribute thousands of dollars to pay off the Seahawks' indebtedness. For most of the owners it was a painful chore but a wise one, for it gained public admiration for the integrity and honesty of the AAC.

Baltimore, under the leadership of Robert R. Rodenberg, was awarded the eighth franchise. Commissioner Crowley resigned to become general manager of the Rockets and was replaced by Admiral Jonas H. Ingram, former commander in chief of the Atlantic Fleet.

CHAPTER 4

Cadets, Controversy, and Bridesmaids Again

THE first controversy that involved Tony Morabito was a lulu. It started in January of 1947 when it was learned that he would attempt to sign West Point's superb "Mr. Outside" and "Mr. Inside" duo—Glenn Davis and Felix (Doc) Blanchard—to 49er contracts. The salary figures were reported as $35,000 each.

The club had taken a flier on Davis in the AAC draft and arranged a trade with Brooklyn for the draft rights to Blanchard. It was a headline story from coast to coast and the verbal fireworks weren't long in exploding. Tony's explanation of the move was all but buried as congressmen, sports writers and editorial pundits sounded off.

"It's my understanding," Tony said, "that Davis and Blanchard will receive a routine ninety-day furlough when they get their commissions in June. They think it would be possible to delay the furloughs until later. Thus, with Army permission, they could play for us during the regular season schedule in September, October and November."

It was an audacious move; and no doubt any park where the two Cadets appeared would have been jammed. They were the most highly publicized players of their era.

The howls of protest—"unmitigated gall . . . unadulterated crust"—carried up to the highest echelons. The War Department finally put the lid on with this statement:

"The requirements of military training and service for young officers are such that the War Department cannot favorably consider granting extended leave of absence for engaging in private enterprise."

The Davis-Blanchard affair had hardly cooled off when the San Francisco papers erupted with the story that Albert wanted to be traded to Los Angeles.

"My home has always been in Southern California," Frankie was quoted as saying, "and I've been offered some fine opportunities in the real estate business. To capitalize on them, I'd have to live in the Los Angeles area."

Telephone calls and letters poured into the 49er office as fans begged Tony and Buck not to let Frankie get away.

Tony's personal feeling was one of exasperation, not worry. He knew that Albert was pulling a colossal bluff in order to get a raise in pay. Frank had signed a three-year contract in 1946 but felt he deserved a higher figure for the second season. Tony, a wily poker player, bluffed right back. News leaked out that the 49ers were willing to trade Albert to the Dons for quarterback Charlie O'Rourke and center Bob Nelson. Tony sat back and awaited a telephone call. It came the next day.

"Hey, Boss," said Albert, "what's going on? Don't you want me any more?"

"You left-handed screwball! You're not fooling me a bit."

"Aw, calm down, Tony. You know I don't want to play for anyone but you."

"Then shut up and start thinking how we can get a winner. See you in July."

A few days later, Albert opened his mail and found himself holding a new contract. It called for a $2,500 raise.

The 49ers launched the 1947 season in auspicious fashion, winning their first three games. But by midseason, the football facts of life were staring Shaw in the face.

"We just don't have the horses to compete with the Browns and Yankees," he said.

The seasonal mark was 8–4–2, with all the losses suffered at the hands of Cleveland and New York. In truth, the club had counted too heavily on much the same personnel that was around in 1946.

Of the six rookies who attained the thirty-five-man roster, only Eddie Carr, a defensive halfback, showed promise of future greatness. Carr, a Philadelphian, never played college ball. During training camp Wally Yonamine, an American of Japanese ancestry from Hawaii, had displayed tremendous breakaway talents. "Fumbleitis" hit him when the regular games started and he spent most of the season on the bench.

A game with Los Angeles almost had tragic overtones. Standlee always played with a huge wad of snuff tucked in his cheek. On a plunge into the line he was hit hard by several Don tacklers. The snuff disappeared down Norm's throat—and so did his tongue.

His jaws locked; he couldn't breathe. Dr. Wilbur Cox, the team physician, grabbed a scalpel and prepared to perform an emergency tracheotomy. But just in time Norm's teeth came unclenched and his breathing resumed.

The classy Browns again finished ahead of the 49ers in the Western Division with a remarkable 12–1–1 record and polished off the Yankees, 14–3, in the championship game.

During the winter of 1948, Al Ruffo resigned as a member of the 49er coaching staff. Even the indefatigable Al had found that coaching, practicing law and serving as a council-man and mayor of San Jose was too big a load.

Shaw made a ten-strike in picking his successor—Eddie Erdelatz, who had been on the Naval Academy staff for two years. Eddie had been a household byword in the Bay Area when he played end for St. Mary's in the mid-1930's.

As usual, there was an off-season controversy—this time in-volving the awarding of Sunday dates at Kezar Stadium, which was also the home field for St. Mary's, Santa Clara, and the University of San Francisco.

There was no denying that the colleges, particularly St. Mary's during the nineteen-year reign of Edward P. (Slip) Madigan, a truly great promoter, had built up Sunday foot-ball in San Francisco. The Catholic schools couldn't face the Saturday competition afforded by powerful California and Stanford.

The 49ers were charged with trying to force the "Inde-pendents" out of football by grabbing the choicest dates. The seriousness of the accusation was compounded by the fact that it also inferred stupidity on the part of the pros. College foot-ball is the life's blood of the play-for-pay organizations.

The writers who waxed indignant would have done well to consult the Kezar files. They showed a steady decline in at-tendance for the Independents after Madigan departed from the picture in 1939. St. Mary's had a brief postwar renais-sance with the Herman Wedemeyer teams but "Squirmin' Herman" ended his collegiate career in 1947.

In one of his rare public utterances a few years ago, Madi-gan put the blame for the fadeout of the Independents on the "freeze-out" schedule adopted by the Pacific Coast Con-ference in 1935. The Independents simply couldn't line up enough bread-and-butter games with PCC schools.

No major schools would play on Sundays; the Independents couldn't draw on Saturday even with such titans as Oklahoma, Michigan State, and Purdue.

Attorney Marshall Leahy represented the 49ers in the hearings before the Park and Recreation Commission and pointed out that four of the seven Sunday dates requested by the club for 1948 would precede or follow the regular college season.

The 49ers were awarded the dates and the way was paved for the team and season that proved pro football was in San Francisco to stay.

CHAPTER **5**

The Runaway Rookies of 1948

SHAW's decision to rebuild the 49ers was borne out at the 1948 training camp. Only twenty of the thirty-five-man 1947 squad were present. They found themselves looking at thirty-eight hungry rookies.

The AAC had voted to reduce rosters to thirty-three, for the league was beginning to feel the pinch of the long and costly war with the NFL. If it was any comfort, some clubs in the older circuit also were wondering where additional funds could be obtained.

The Silver Fox cracked the whip daily and there were long, sometimes violent, scrimmages.

The veterans, as is their wont in any professional sport, signed a mutual assistance pact: they were going to show the upstart newcomers how tough real pros were. They picked Hal Shoener, a shy, soft-spoken defensive end from Iowa, as their first victim.

Albert flipped the ball to Johnny Strike, who headed around the flank behind a convoy of eager pals. What happened next can best be described as an explosion. The ball went one way, Strike another, and two blockers were stretched out on the turf.

"Holy smoke!" gasped Vetrano. "Don't send *me* around there. That guy's got six elbows!"

When the final cut was made, seventeen rookies, probably an all-time pro record, and sixteen veterans survived. Of the seventeen, seven became notable performers in the years to follow. Besides Shoener, they were Verl Lillywhite, half-back-fullback, U.S.C.; Gail Bruce, end, Washington; Jim Cason, halfback, Louisiana State; Don Clark, linebacker, U.S.C.; Bill Johnson, center, Tyler, Texas, Junior College; and Joe Perry, fullback, Compton, California, Junior College.

At a practice session, Shaw noticed Cason throwing passes with both his left and right hands. He asked which hand the stringbean Texan would use in a game.

"My right," Jim replied. "It's stronger with a football. But I was a southpaw pitcher for L.S.U. I batted left-handed, too, but I play golf right-handed."

"Are you a right or left halfback?" Buck inquired.

"Both," said Jim.

Then he got off a long punt with his left foot.

The exciting season in store for the 49ers was forecast by exhibition wins over Los Angeles, 42–24, and Baltimore, 42–14. A balding rookie quarterback, Yelberton Abraham Tittle, was the only Colt who had moments of glory.

Albert had never looked better, leading sports editor McDonald to write:

Quite possibly the 28-year-old Frankie has all the "cold" days out of his system now that he has finally decided to make a career out of pro football. Until this season, Albert split his vision between a construction business and football. He started each season with the thought that it would be his last. But this year he has forgotten his outside interests.

The regular season commenced with easy wins over Buffalo and Brooklyn. Perry's 58-yard touchdown run against the Bills the first time he ever carried the ball in a league game made opponents wonder how they were going to stop the 200-pound Negro boy who had been timed in 9.6 for the century dash.

The Yankees, who had never lost to the 49ers in four meetings, were next and San Francisco, for the first time, went pro football crazy. An overflow crowd of 60,927 (now impossible because of stricter fire department regulations) poured into Kezar and screamed with happy frenzy as the team demolished New York, 41–0.

"Holy criminy!" a shaken Yankee coach said after the game. "Those guys are mad dogs!"

During the game, some of the photographers on the sideline told Albert they hadn't been able to get any good close-up shots.

"We'll take care of that on the next play," said Frankie, not caring that the Yankees could hear him. "I'll pitch out to Strike and he'll head right for you."

The play developed just as Albert described it, the photographers got their picture—and Strike picked up a big chunk of yardage.

It was the beginning of a ten-game victory string—longest in 49er history. Albert directed the club with a daring that was almost insulting to opponents. His passing was sharper than ever before, and his now-you-see-it, now-you-don't magic with the football became legendary.

The rookie fullbacks, Perry and Lillywhite, were both averaging better than five yards per carry. Their quick development permitted Shaw to move Standlee to defense where his 240 pounds shored up serious linebacking deficiencies.

Johnny Strike had the best ball-packing average in the

Johnny "Strike" Strzykalski

league, close to seven yards. Beals, a triple-feint artist, was making impossible catches.

Over-all, the club was averaging 38 points per game and 426 yards total offense. Small wonder that for the first time applications for championship game tickets were being received by the front office.

So the stage was set for the "crucial" at Cleveland on November 14. The Browns, playing one less game, had been victorious nine straight times.

Cleveland fans established a new pro attendance record when 82,769 of them walked through the turnstiles at Municipal Stadium that afternoon. If they expected a wild, offensive battle, they were disappointed.

Forrest Hall, the little 49er scatback, fumbled the opening kickoff on the 10-yard line, the Browns recovered and scored in two plays.

Hall, practically in tears, was the most surprised man on the bench when Shaw sent him in, instead of Eshmont, the regular left halfback, the next time the 49ers got the ball. It was Shaw's way of telling Hall to forget his miscue.

The 49ers drove 80 yards to deadlock the game and it was 7–7 at half time. Cleveland acquired the go-ahead touchdown in the third quarter, and that was how it ended, 14–7. Two other fumbles halted 49er marches but the Browns dominated most of the game. They ruined Albert's aerial streak, holding him to 32 yards in six completions.

The sting of the defeat was partly salved the following Sunday when the boys crushed the Dodgers at Brooklyn, 63–40. The 49ers amassed 547 yards passing and running.

The club headed back to San Francisco for the all-important rematch with Cleveland. In midweek, the 49ers were quoted as six-point favorites and there was an immediate uproar that a "fix" was on. A San Francisco victory, of course, would have deadlocked the standings, forcing a lucrative play-off at Cleveland if both teams, as expected, finished the schedule without another loss.

Sports writers pointed out the reason for the 49ers being favored—Otto Graham, Cleveland's celebrated passer, had been injured the previous week. They couldn't stop the vicious rumors.

When the Browns came out of the tunnel for the pre-game warm-up, everyone in the sell-out crowd knew Cleveland had told the truth about Graham's leg injury. He was limping badly and could barely pivot for hand-offs.

The game was an epic. The Browns cashed in quickly on two 49er fumbles for 10 points. Overcoming their jitters, the San Franciscans scored twice in the second period. The second touchdown was set up by Johnny Strike's unbelievable 29-yard run when he was battered to the ground two times but fought to his feet and kept going.

Trailing by four points at the half, the Browns dominated the third quarter with three touchdowns to the 49ers' one. With seven minutes to play, San Francisco made another. They couldn't get the ball again until too late. Title hopes went down the drain, 31–28.

Prescott Sullivan of the *Examiner* asked Tony how much the clubs would have made out of a play-off.

"About $50,000 each," Tony said. "But I'm almost glad the play-off is out. To me, it's worth that much to make the wise guys shut up."

Sports editor Bud Spencer of the *News* wrote:

Whatever happend to the weisenheimers who whispered that it was San Francisco's turn to win over Cleveland? As it turned out, it was a game of games, strictly for keeps, and a rugged afternoon for the finer qualities of manhood.

It was the height of frustration for the 49ers to finish the season 12–2 and still be second best to the Browns. Buffalo, after defeating Baltimore in a play-off, won the Eastern Division with an 8–7 mark and was massacred, 49–7, by Cleveland.

It was a glorious year statistically. The rookie-studded 49ers established pro records of 3,663 yards rushing, 5,767 yards total offense, 65 touchdowns and 495 total points.

Albert threw 29 touchdown passes, a new major league mark, with Beals on the receiving end of 14. *Sport* magazine named Frankie "Pro Player of the Year."

Johnny Strike had his finest campaign, finishing second in rushing with 915 yards. Perry ate up 562 yards on 77 carries and his 7.3 average was tops in the AAC.

Financially, the outlook was not heartening. The big crowds at home couldn't make up for small ones on the road. Operational costs had jumped considerably and the accountants were still using red ink.

CHAPTER 6

"It's the 49ers in '49"
— Almost

EARLY in 1949, Tony took a deep breath and made his biggest gamble—he and Vic took over complete ownership of the 49ers on a 75–25 basis. Then, to get operating capital during the off season, he borrowed $100,000.

All of his worldly goods were tied up in the club. His house was heavily mortgaged.

Close friends shook their heads sadly and expressed concern about his sanity. Peace talks between the AAC and NFL in late December had ended with recriminations and bitterness. The Associated Press quoted an NFL official as saying no agreement could be reached because the AAC wanted to bring in "weak sisters" if a merger was formulated. He identified one of the "weak sisters" as Baltimore. Shades of Johnny Unitas!

The AAC's shaky status became more evident when the Brooklyn franchise was merged with New York. The Chicago Rockets, renamed the Hornets, had their fourth set of owners in as many years. It was an open secret, however, that the Hornets were kept alive by monetary injections from the Los Angeles Croesus, Lindheimer.

Tony argued that with Chicago strengthened by the addition of some Brooklyn personnel, the AAC would display an improved caliber of play. With only seven clubs, there could be no divisional setup, so it was decided to play a round-robin schedule with the top two clubs at the end of the season meeting for the championship.

Getting down to the more agreeable task of building a winner, Tony signed Albert to a $20,000 contract. It was a typical gesture for the 49er owner who had financial disaster staring him in the face. He took pride in the fact that Albert, in all probability, was the highest-paid player in pro football.

Asked if Albert was worthy of the sum, Shaw said:

"I don't think he can be beaten. He has great imagination and is a born leader. He is the best ball handler I've ever seen. He is an outstanding passer and kicker.

"I wouldn't trade him for Otto Graham of Cleveland. If we could give Frankie the protection and receivers that Graham is supplied with, he would outpass Otto. Frankie has the peculiar knack of inspiring confidence. The team thinks that everything he does is the right and proper thing, which is a quarterback's greatest asset.

"He's liked by everyone. He never blames a lineman for missing a block or an end for muffing a pass. I don't see how you could improve upon him."

Training camp that year was enlivened by the arrival of Bill (The Knee) Pacheco, a ukulele-playing, barefooted place kicker from Honolulu. At thirty-two, The Knee didn't expect to indulge in bodily contact, but he was firmly convinced he was the world's greatest place-kicking specialist, shoeless or shod.

He presented a Hawaiian shirt to "Little Toe" Vetrano

and declared: "This is a token of my admiration and esteem for you. Please don't be jealous when Shaw selects me to kick the field goals and extra points."

The Knee filled out the club's publicity questionnaire thusly:

Your favorite sports hero: Myself, naturally.
Hobbies: Reading newspaper clippings about myself.
Accomplishments: Doing the hula when I kick a field goal or extra point.

In the first intrasquad game, The Knee played for the "Reds" and kicked all the conversions as they defeated the "Whites," 28–0. After each kick he went into his dance and turned handsprings all the way back to the bench. Even Shaw, always deadly serious about football, had to smile.

The Knee was en route home several days later, but he had his memories. He and his wife now own one of Honolulu's most popular night clubs; The Knee plays the uke and guitar, sings in Japanese, Hawaiian, and Portuguese, and acts as master of ceremonies.

Perry, nicknamed "The Jet" by his teammates, was more impressive daily. Albert told a newsman:

"Joe has the best future of anybody in pro football today. He'll be the greatest fullback in the history of the game."

The rookie crop again was promising, with special attention focused on Paul Salata, end, U.S.C.; Homer Hobbs, guard, Georgia; Pete Wismann, linebacker, St. Louis U.; and Sam Cathcart, halfback, Santa Barbara State.

The club's slogan was "It's the 49ers in '49" and on the sunny afternoon of October 9 the idea became a distinct probability. San Francisco had won four out of five league games; Cleveland was 4–0–1. The Browns hadn't suffered a loss in thirty-one consecutive AAC games.

The San Francisco faithful, ever hopeful, again had Kezar

bulging at the seams and the club estimated it had to return orders for another 40,000 tickets.

Six minutes after the opening kickoff Albert pitched a 16-yard touchdown pass to Strzykalski. Two minutes later another southpaw aerial to Beals gained 42 yards and Strike plunged over from the one-yard line.

Before the first period ended, Shoener pounced on a fumble by the Browns on their own 28. Albert passed to Perry who made a spectacular one-handed catch for the third touchdown.

Cleveland went to work and scored twice as the fans stopped shouting and looked at each other uneasily. They needn't have worried. Shoener bulled in and knocked the ball out of Graham's grasp on the Browns' 16 and Albert, on the next play, found Beals standing alone in the end zone.

Cleveland fought back as Graham connected with a 61-yard heave to Dub Jones and covered the rest of the distance with a 13-yard pass to Mac Speedie. Before the half ended, the 49ers drove 63 yards, with Albert faking a bootleg run and pegging the ball 8 yards to Nick Susoeff for the tally that brought the score to 35–21.

In the third quarter, Albert's fifth touchdown pass, this time to Eddie Carr, made it 42–21. The Browns scored as the fourth quarter opened, but this was their last gasp. Perry broke their backs when he shot off right tackle and raced 49 yards without being touched. The Brown's debacle was closed out at 56–28 when Carr dived over the goal from 5 yards out.

Perry totaled 156 yards on 16 carries for a 9-yard average. In all, the 49ers gained 561 yards passing and running.

Glenn S. (Pop) Warner, who viewed the game from the press box, told the writers: "On this day, the 49ers were the greatest football team I have ever seen."

It was New Year's Eve all over again in San Francisco that night. The delirious fans whooped it up in the restaurants and bars and interminable toasts were drunk to the heroes of the gridiron.

The jubilation lasted exactly seven days or, more exactly, to the moment that Johnny Strike was placed on a stretcher and carried off the field. His left leg was broken and he was out for the season. Buffalo was slaughtered, 51–7, but the stands were strangely quiet. Buck had tagged Strike as the "best right halfback in football." More than that, he was the embodiment of the fighting 49er spirit.

Carr injured his knee in the same game. At first it wasn't thought serious, yet it ended his career.

Gloomily, the 49ers boarded a plane for New York, where they were humiliated by the Yankees, 24–3. No one was comforted by the crowd of 36,197—6,000 more than the Giants and Chicago Bears drew in an NFL clash the same day at the Polo Grounds.

Perry gained only 16 yards in 9 carries.

"They didn't have to worry about Strike and were able to gang up on Joe," Buck explained. "It's no use trying to kid ourselves. We've been trying to operate on one wheel since we lost Strike and Carr."

The dirge continued at Cleveland as the Browns, determined to avenge their trouncing in San Francisco, took a 30–28 decision. A 38-yard field goal by Lou Groza in the fourth period was the clincher.

The "old pros," particularly Standlee and Eshmont, pulled the club together for victories over Baltimore and Los Angeles. The 49ers never lost to the Dons in AAC competition —eight games.

Returning to the friendly confines of Kezar, they gained revenge on the Yankees in the season's finale, 35–14. This gave both clubs 9–3 records and a second-place tie, forcing a play-off to determine Cleveland's foe in the championship tussle.

Monday was an off day, but the players held a meeting and

decided they should receive an extra game salary because of the play-off. They named Standlee and Eshmont as their representatives.

"Read your contracts," snapped Tony when the emissaries appeared at his office Tuesday morning. "You played only twelve league games this year instead of fourteen and the contract specifies a play-off game if necessary."

Practice was skipped that day as the players held a second meeting. They wouldn't budge.

Tony's answer was swift and to the point: "If you aren't out on the field tomorrow morning at ten o'clock, we'll forfeit the game to the Yankees. Furthermore, you'll be fined twenty-five per cent of your salaries."

Not a soul was missing when Shaw blew the whistle for practice the next morning. And the Yankees were vanquished, 17–7.

The title game was slated for Cleveland on Sunday, December 11. The 49ers, with visions of a huge crowd and lucrative shares of the gate, arrived in the Ohio metropolis Friday night. The first thing they saw at the airport was a newspaper banner line announcing that the AAC had merged with the NFL.

The game was strictly an anticlimax. It was played in snow and slush and only 22,550 fans were interested enough to watch the Browns win, 21–7. Each Cleveland player received $266.11; each 49er, $172.61.

It was a sad ending to four years of hard work.

The over-all record for the AAC campaigns was 38–14–2. Cleveland was 47–4–3.

There was one happy note. The 49ers finally showed a profit in 1949. True, it was a small profit, but Tony and Vic figured it was a turning point.

CHAPTER 7

"Not Big Enough or Tough Enough"

APPOMATTOX Courthouse was probably a friendlier place on April 9, 1865, than Philadelphia, Pennsylvania, on the 18th of January, 1950.

Some of the men who gathered at the conference table had exchanged harsh words during the four years of the pro football war. The three surviving All-America Conference clubs —Cleveland, San Francisco, and Baltimore—quickly learned that it was a surrender, not a merger, as far as a number of powerful NFL owners were concerned. They found just as quickly that they would receive fair treatment from rotund, gravel-voiced Commissioner Bert Bell of the National Football League.

The meeting was deadlocked for almost three days over what to do with the players of the defunct AAC teams and the college seniors drafted by them the previous month. There was also a bitter hassle over reserve lists. A few clubs had built up large backlogs of talent by drafting players for future delivery. (In pro parlance they are known as "redshirts.")

Bell patiently let the owners argue themselves out. As he expected, they finally tossed the issues into his lap. His decisions were:

1. All college seniors, including those who had already signed with various clubs, would be placed in the draft pool.

2. Most of the players from the defunct AAC teams would be pooled and then selected at a special draft meeting in June.

3. The clubs could select only three players from their reserve lists. Everyone else was draftable.

"His decisions were fair and square to everybody," Tony said. "I think he did a magnificent job."

When the schedule was discussed, some owners balked at going to the Pacific Coast because, they claimed, 49er and Ram ticket prices were too low. The 49ers had been charging $3.60 for seats between the 30- and 50-yard lines; $2.40 for other reserved seats; $1.80 for general admission and 50 cents for children under twelve.

George Preston Marshall of the Washington Redskins was especially voluble on the subject.

"It's an imposition on eastern clubs to make them travel to the coast," he told Curley Grieve of the *Examiner*. "Personally, I never want to go out there for league games. So it's up to San Francisco and Los Angeles to compensate other teams for that long, hard and expensive trip. They'll have to raise their prices."

Tony did hike the tariff to $3.75, $3 and $2, maintaining the 50 cents for youngsters. But 49er prices were still the lowest in the league and held that distinction until 1958.

Shaw's first three picks in the draft were big tackles—Leo Nomellini, six feet three, 255 pounds, Minnesota; Don Campora, six feet three, 270, College of Pacific; and Ray Collins, six feet, 235, Louisiana State. The emphasis on this position

was necessary because John Woudenberg and Bob Bryant, who had carried the load offensively and defensively during all four years of the AAC, had both retired.

In the divisional picture, the 49ers were placed in what was called the National Conference, along with the Chicago Bears, Green Bay, Los Angeles, New York Yanks, and Detroit. The American Conference included the New York Giants, Chicago Cardinals, Cleveland, Washington, Pittsburgh, and Philadelphia. The Baltimore Colts were the "swing" team, playing every other club in the league.

Jack McDonald charged in his "Both Barrels" column in the *Call-Bulletin* that the 49ers had been shoved into the weaker division. "The strong and colorful teams are all in the American Conference," he said. "Detroit, ugh! Green Bay, double ugh! A shabby trick has been played on San Francisco fans."

Before the season started, the 49ers had to locate a line coach to replace Erdelatz, who had gone to the Naval Academy as head coach. Eddie took Eshmont and Don Clark along as his assistants.

Shaw wasted no time in signing Charles (Chuck) Taylor who had been singularly successful as Stanford's freshman coach.

A newspaper story quoted Albert as saying he would be a holdout again, and Frankie fired back through Bud Spencer of the *News:*

"I've never been happier in my life, and the main thought in my mind has been concerned with getting a crack at those National Leaguers. Then I read that I'm an agitator. Heck, I've worked for Tony Morabito for four years and he's always been more than fair with me. I think my teammates feel the same way.

"Take that so-called strike of last year. It was just a case of the story leaking out while everything was still in a discussion stage. I've only discussed next year's contract with Tony once. The next time I'll probably sign.

"Let's keep the record clear. In 1946 I signed a three-year contract. At the end of a year Tony tore up the contract and gave me a raise. Two years later I got another raise. Where could you find a better business relationship?"

When one columnist called him the "Branch Rickey of football," Tony said: "That was meant to be a knock. I regard it as the highest compliment I've ever received. I wish I was as smart as Rickey."

Season ticket sales climbed to 10,000—more than double the previous high—as the Bay Area fans became more excited over the prospect of seeing NFL fans and stars. They were confident the 49ers would more than hold their own in the merged league.

Many veteran football observers agreed with this belief and several predicted in magazine and newspaper articles that the championship play-off would be between the old AAC rivals, Cleveland and San Francisco.

Early training camp reports boosted the stock of rookies Collins and three U.S.C. alumni—Don (Boom Boom) Burke, fullback-linebacker; Jimmy Powers, quarterback-defensive halfback; and Jack Nix, offensive end. Nomellini, Campora, and Emil (Six-Yard) Sitko of Notre Dame were late arrivals after helping the College All-Stars upset the Philadelphia Eagles in Chicago, 17–7.

The 49ers were enjoying their clippings, particularly the comments about how they would breeze through NFL opposition. Tony was as cocky as the players. Before the opening exhibition game at Kezar with the Washington Redskins, he told Shaw:

"Pour it on, Buck! If you get forty points, shoot for eighty!"

What happened was probably best summed up by Bruce Lee in the *Chronicle:*

Hey, maybe they should revive the All-America Conference. Either this National Football League is a pretty tough outfit, as represented today by the Washington Redskins, or an ain't-got-it San Francisco 49er team has started winding on a long, long trail. The Redskins won, 31 to 21, before 51,201 people who weren't happy at all about this, the San Franciscans' debut in the NFL. For the men from Washington were clearly superior in every department of play, a bitter T-leaf for the perennial second-best team of the old AAC to swallow.

Compounding the shame, the 49ers failed to convert after both of their touchdowns. A cry went up for "Little Toe" Vetrano who had been released during training camp because he was regarded as strictly a kicking specialist.

During the gloomy days that followed, the club came up with the best trade in its history, obtaining Gordy Soltau of Minnesota from Cleveland for a fourth-draft choice. Besides being an expert place kicker, the tall Norwegian from Duluth also became one of the great pass receivers in the league during his nine-year career.

As far as NFL competition was concerned, shock followed upon shock. The defending champion Philadelphia Eagles, disdaining the use of Steve Van Buren, their All-Pro fullback, romped to a 28–10 victory over the demoralized 49er forces. The team thankfully left town for a three-week trip and temporarily revived by beating the Colts at Baltimore.

But there were further disasters at Chicago and Pittsburgh. The 49ers led the Cardinals, 21–7, with seven minutes to play. Then quarterback Jim Hardy connected for three touchdown passes, two to Bob Shaw, later to become a 49er assistant coach. Final score: Cardinals 28, 49ers 21.

The San Franciscans led Pittsburgh, 10–0, going into the fourth quarter. The Steelers pulled it out, 13–10.

The sorry 1–4 exhibition record was an indication of sadder things to come. The club lost five straight league games before shading Detroit, 28–27, at San Francisco. After a 35–14

Gordy Soltau

humiliation by Los Angeles, a Ram coach declared: "The 49ers aren't big enough or tough enough for the National League."

The seasonal record of 3–9 was and still is the worst in the club's history. Yet an analysis of the twelve games shows another four or five victories were missed by a few points or a few inches.

"That still rates as my favorite 49er team," says Soltau. "Everything seemed to go against us, but we never threw in the towel. We had wonderful *esprit de corps* and most of us couldn't wait until we got organized for 1951 and had another shot at the clubs that were laughing at us."

Gordy and his cohorts got their chance. The only trouble was, they didn't realize until too late how good they were.

Joe Arenas (82) eludes Emerson Cole (70) and runs 32 yards in 24—10 upset of Cleveland

CHAPTER 8

The Tough Guys of 1951

In January of 1951, the Baltimore franchise was turned back to the NFL and all Colt players were placed in the regular draft pool. The prize plum of the list was Yelberton Abraham Tittle, who had gained critical acclaim during his three frustrating seasons with outmanned Baltimore squads.

The New York Giants had the bonus choice and selected Kyle Rote of Southern Methodist. The Chicago Bears were next in line, having Baltimore's first pick from a previous trade, and tagged Bob Williams, the Notre Dame quarterback.

Louis G. (Lucky Lou) Spadia, the 49er general manager, was involved in the flip of a coin with Green Bay and Washington, which also had 3–9 marks in 1950. Spadia, as usual, was victorious and the 49ers chose Tittle.

Shaw must have been blessed with an extra amount of Irish

good fortune, for he came up with what was undoubtedly the finest draft in 49er annals. His list, besides Tittle, included Pete Schabarum, Al Carapella, Rex Berry, Nick Feher, Joe Arenas, Jim Monachino, Bill Jessup, Bobby White, Dave Sparks, Bishop Strickland, and Hardy Brown.

Brown, a twenty-third choice, had played for Washington and Baltimore after several years with Chicago in the All-America Conference. There have been better all-around linebackers in pro football than Brown, but no one has ever matched him for instilling pure fear in opposing ball carriers.

Brown's weapon was a "shoulder tackle," and like a guided missile it seemed to seek out the chin of an ambitious runner. There was nothing illegal about the tackle, but it was much criticized by opponents—especially halfbacks. On more than one occasion, other teams sent game officials into the 49er dressing room to check Brown's shoulder pads: they believed such wicked blows could not be delivered without some type of metal reinforcement. They were wrong.

In Tittle's words, "Hardy would pop that shoulder at his best friend—if the guy was carrying a football."

The pre-season schedule began with a 45–14 "revenge" win over Washington. The Bears were a stumbling block again, but the loss to them was followed by victories over Pittsburgh, Green Bay, and the Chicago Cardinals.

The Cardinal game at Omaha had an important bearing on what happened during the regular season. The 49ers, having spent ten peaceful days at Father Flanagan's Boys' Town in Omaha, were like a pack of wild men by the time they met the Cardinals. If ever a team took a physical beating, it was the Chicagoans. They didn't forget—or forgive.

The opening league game was a delight; the defending world champion Browns were defeated, 24 to 10. Two interceptions by linebacker Pete Wismann led to 49er touchdowns. Rookie end Billy Wilson, drafted the previous year as a "fu-

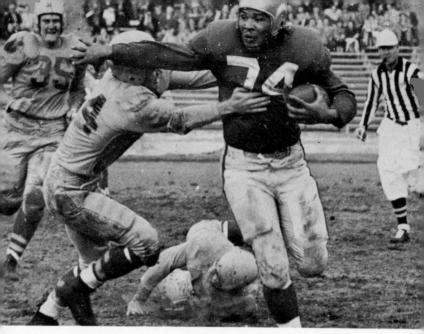

Joe "Jet" Perry rips 22 yards through Green Bay for a touchdown

ture," caught his first 49er scoring pass. Lillywhite, used on a new "trap" play designed by Shaw, gained 145 yards on 17 carries.

Buck knew he had pressing problems to solve before the club would be a solid contender. Albert had injured his shoulder against the Browns and could barely lob the ball; Tittle was still learning the basic elements of the Shaw system.

"My biggest headache is with Perry," said Y. A. "He takes off so fast that I'm still holding the ball on what is supposed to be a hand-off when the Jet is twenty yards down the field."

A three-week road trip resulted in one-touchdown losses to the Eagles and the Bears and a wild 28–24 decision over the Steelers. But the 2–2 standing kept the 49ers in the race and they vowed to beat the Rams for the first time.

Even Shaw caught the enthusiasm of his swashbuckling, spirited crew. "This team won't admit anyone else is better,"

Buck told Bill Anderson of the *News*. "They're playing for keeps—and the title."

The '51 Rams were, without a doubt, one of the greatest pro teams ever assembled. They had speed, power, and magnificent passing with Bob Waterfield and Norm Van Brocklin throwing to Crazy-Legs Hirsch, Bob Boyd, Tom Fears and other fine receivers.

The final tally of 44–17, favoring the 49ers, made football fans all over the country blink with amazement. Soltau had the best afternoon of his illustrious career, scoring 26 points on three touchdown receptions, a field goal, and 5 extra points.

Nomellini realized every lineman's dream. He blocked a punt by Van Brocklin on the Ram 30, chased the ball into the end zone and fell on it for 6 points. The 49er defense picked off six Los Angeles passes.

The uninhibited Grgich spent a pleasant afternoon making life miserable for Van Brocklin. The Dutchman finally blew his top and challenged Visco to a fight after the game.

"Sorry," replied Grgich, "I'm a coward!"

Shaw had taken a calucated gamble in endeavoring to overcome the Rams' big advantage in speed. He had Jim Powers and Verl Lillywhite working as outside linebackers, while Brown and his shoulder took care of the middle. This trio averaged under 190 pounds but the strategy paid off. The deep backs—Cason, Wagner and Berry—didn't have to worry too much about the Rams running outside.

Head coach Joe Stydahar of the Rams and his chief aide, Red Hickey, found the answer to the pony linebackers when the rematch was played the following Sunday at Los Angeles. They devised a "Bull Elephant" backfield of three fullbacks—Dan Towler, Tank Younger and Dick Hoerner. When Shaw tried to counter by replacing Powers and Lillywhite with Burke and Standlee, both 240-pounders, Stydahar sent in the speedy Vitamin Smith and Glenn Davis. Ultimately, three field goals by Waterfield decided the issue in favor of the Rams, 23–16.

A weak New York Yanks team had the 49ers on the ropes in the seventh game; but Tittle hit Wilson with a scoring pass in the final forty-six seconds for a 19–14 victory.

What Shaw had feared now became a reality. The fans divided into Albert and Tittle camps and there was blood-letting in some of the town's better saloons as arguments passed the talking stage.

"I knew that inevitably we were going to get into this squeeze," Shaw told Bruce Lee. "It's the same thing in Los Angeles where they have Waterfield and Van Brocklin. One or the other is always on the pan with the fans and the press . . . or else the coaches are."

Meanwhile, the Chicago Cardinals, still smarting over the pasting they had taken at Omaha in the exhibition game, arrived in town.

The situation was ripe for an upset. Tony and Vic didn't help any when they predicted publicly that the 49ers would win the rest of their games—and the championship. It was more fuel for the Cardinal fire.

At half time, the Chicagoans led, 24–7, and Shaw was steaming as he addressed his club in the locker room. There was a marked improvement in the second half, but the Cardinals hung on for a 27–21 upset.

The Yanks added additional humiliation when they gained a 10–10 deadlock in New York, but the 49ers bounced back into the race when they stopped the Lions, 20–10, at Detroit. In this game, Shaw sent Tittle into the line-up in the fourth quarter with orders to stay on the ground and protect the 10-point lead.

Y. A.'s first call was a long pass, incomplete; so was the second. Shaw, practically apoplectic, was summoning Albert

Frankie Albert gets off pass against Detroit

to go back in when Tittle, of his own volition, came running to the bench. "I'm sorry, coach," he declared, "I just want some more touchdowns. Those guys almost killed me when I was with Baltimore."

The final home stand of 1951 began with an easy win over Green Bay. Detroit defeated Los Angeles and came into San Francisco needing a victory to take the Western Conference crown. The Lions were 7–3–1, the Rams 7–4, and the 49ers 6–4–1. The 49ers had an outside chance, hinging on a Green Bay shocker in Los Angeles.

With four minutes to go, the Lions led, 17–14. Then Arenas grabbed a punt on the dead run and raced 51 yards to the Detroit nine. Tittle executed a perfect bootleg maneuver and made the winning touchdown standing up. The roar that went up at Kezar was echoed at Memorial Coliseum in Los Angeles by happy Ram fans.

Hugh McElhenny

CHAPTER **9**

Folly on Fourth Down

BEFORE Tony Morabito headed east for the NFL draft meeting in January of 1952, he received a telephone call from Frank Albert in Honolulu. Typically, the left-hander called at two o'clock in the morning—collect.

Groggily Tony delivered himself of a few comments on Albert's telephone habits, then snapped into wakefulness. Albert actually apologized for the late call, he'd forgotten the two-hour time differential. And his words were deadly serious: "I played in the Hula Bowl today against the greatest running back I've ever seen—Hugh McElhenny. Tony, we've got to get him!"

The 49er owner knew that Albert, despite his screwball tendencies, was a good judge of football talent. Although McElhenny had been a star at the University of Washington, some coaches and scouts claimed he was not temperamentally suited for pro ball—a "problem child," one report said.

The 49ers, of course, had the pleasure of discovering later

how erroneous those reports were. In most instances, they were based on idle and vicious gossip.

Shaw had personally scouted McElhenny and wanted him but believed that the 49ers, who would draft eighth, didn't have a chance of landing him. The Rams had the bonus pick and took Bill Wade of Vanderbilt. Then the draft went like this:

Chicago Cardinals—Ollie Matson; Green Bay—Babe Parilli; Pittsburgh—Ed Modzelewski; Dallas—Les Richter; Washington—Larry Isbell; Chicago Bears—Jim Dooley; New York—Frank Gifford.

So McElhenny was there for the 49ers.

After the comeback of 1951, Tony could hardly wait for the 1952 season to begin. He almost didn't live to see it, for in March he suffered a serious heart attack. A specialist called in by his personal physician, Dr. Bill O'Grady, shook his head sadly after examining Tony and checking the charts.

"It's 60–40 against him," he told Mrs. Jo Morabito. A priest was summoned and Tony received the Last Rites.

But the tough little fellow refused to give up, slowly began to recover. When the immediate danger was passed, the doctors told him he would have to get out of football—"too much tension and pressure for a heart like yours."

He agreed to sell the club, or at least the doctors thought he did. A steady parade of would-be buyers marched in and out of the 49er office. Strangely, when a deal would be just about set, Tony would find some excuse to end negotiations.

He didn't fool Dr. O'Grady for long.

"Let's put the cards on the table," the doctor finally told his patient. "You have no intention of selling."

Tony sheepishly agreed. "I'll be worse off if I get out of football," he said. "What the heck will I do with myself?"

O'Grady smiled and tried again. "You know as well as I do that you're in an emotional business. There is danger in the

Joe Perry on his way to one of four touchdowns against Washington

excitement of winning and the despair of losing. If you want to take the chance, we can't stop you."

So Tony was on borrowed time, and knew it. He only hoped the hours wouldn't run out on him before the 49ers brought a championship to San Francisco.

The veteran players were aware of the situation. They didn't make public vows to "win for Tony," but dropped in frequently to see him during his convalescence and assured him they were ready for the "big effort."

They found his illness had not interrupted his paternal interest in their personal affairs. The player who needed money for family emergencies, or to go into a promising business, knew that Tony would stand behind him. Many a retired 49er started his new career on a loan from Tony.

There was a supercharged atmosphere at training camp in early August of 1952—especially after McElhenny had been introduced to the squad by Albert.

"Men," Frankie said with a grin, "I want you to meet the only college star ever to take a salary cut to play pro football!"

Hugh needed only a few practice sessions to make believers out of his teammates. For the first time the 49ers had a big halfback—198 pounds—with a sprinter's speed. He was deadly serious about succeeding in the pro game, thus refuting the irresponsible claims of his critics.

Shaw, with admirable restraint, told Wally Willis of the Oakland *Tribune:* "McElhenny has every requisite to become a great running back in this league—speed, power, change of pace and a straight arm that is a rarity nowadays. But best of all, he puts out on every play, whether or not he's carrying the ball. He's no blocker—but he tries. The team appreciates that effort more than his ability to run away from or over tacklers."

Hugh made his debut in an exhibition with the Cardinals and ran 60 yards for a touchdown the first time he got his hands on the ball. Albert made up the play in the huddle, a wide pitchout that sprung McElhenny past the line of scrimmage before the defense sensed what was coming.

In seven pre-season appearances, the team eased through five league opponents and two semipro clubs. Season ticket sales climbed to over 6,000, highest ever with the exception of 1950.

The regular schedule appeared ominous because Detroit, building its own gridiron dynasty, had to be faced twice in the first three weeks. Unbelievably, the 49ers shattered the Lions in both games—17–3 at San Francisco and 28–0 at Briggs Stadium.

McElhenny, as expected, was sensational. So was Bob Toneff, 250-pound rookie tackle from Notre Dame.

The second Detroit meeting was highlighted by the appearance of Charlie Powell, a nineteen-year-old free agent from San Diego High School, at defensive end. Powell had professionalized himself by playing baseball in the Class C California League. His diamond career ended abruptly because of his inability to hit the "No. 2" pitch.

Shaw was notified by a friend that Powell might make the grade in pro football. Buck was the most surprised person of all when the six-foot-three, 215-pound colored lad weathered the training camp battles and won a place on the regular season squad.

Injuries had hit the squad and only twenty-eight players were available for duty in Detroit. Line coach Phil Bengtson called Powell aside in the pre-game warm-up and told him he would start at defensive end.

"You only have to remember one thing, Charlie," Bengtson said. "Just drive in and rush Bobby Layne as hard as you can."

"If that's what you say to do, Mr. Bengtson, I'll do it."

Charlie lived up to his instructions so well that Layne, one of the league's all-time passers, failed to complete an aerial until the fourth quarter.

Powell never again came up to that performance as a 49er, although he did put in five seasons with the club in between attempts to become the world's heavyweight boxing champion.

The 49ers went in Wrigley Field with three straight victories and exploded their old Bear jinx, 40–16. McElhenny returned a punt 94 yards for a touchdown with Toneff in front of him all the way and gained 114 yards in 12 carries.

Returning home, the club made it five in a row by overwhelming Dallas again. In the general jubilation, no one noticed—or wanted to—that there were several cracks in the dikes. The fine careers of Gail Bruce and Grgich had been ended by ankle and knee injuries, respectively. Their loss was not felt—until the crucial part of the schedule started.

A dedicated bunch of Bears arrived at Kezar on November 2, 1952. George Halas had not let them forget the humiliation

Wedging 'em out

(Courtesy Oakland Tribune)

at Chicago. But the 49ers, though far from their early-season form, held a 17–10 lead at the beginning of the fourth quarter.

Then came the play that many claim wrecked the team—and the season.

The 49ers had the ball on their own 32-yard line, fourth down and two yards to go. Albert, back to kick, glimpsed a wide opening between defensive right end and tackle. Taking the pass from center, he decided in a split second to run instead of punt. He sped past his own amazed blockers—into the arms of Ed Sprinkle. The wily Bear defensive end had opened that gap deliberately to bait Albert.

The Chicagoans immediately drove to the tying touchdown, and with a minute to go George Blanda kicked a 48-yard field goal to shatter the San Francisco dream, 20–17.

After the game the obvious question was asked Shaw: What did he think of Albert's strategy?

"Frank has won a lot of games for us with his daring," replied Buck. "He's got away with that same gamble many times. That's all I can say."

Actually, the coach was seething inside and the incident put an almost unendurable strain on relations that had become rather tender in the past several seasons. There is no doubt it had much bearing on Albert's surprise decision to retire at the end of the year.

One of the more humorous stories concerning that game involved Buck and Prescott Sullivan of the *Examiner*.

The cigar-chewing columnist called Shaw the week before the game and asked him what he was "going to do about Halas running up and down the sidelines." He quoted the rule permitting coaches to move in an area extending only 10 yards from the middle of the bench.

"The league hasn't done anything about it for thirty-three years," said Shaw. "Who am I to complain?"

That was the extent of the conversation. But Sullivan had a lengthy column in the *Examiner* the next morning, quoting Shaw as saying he was ready to complain to Commissioner Bell about Halas. Buck, according to the story, was going to demand that the officials enforce a 15-yard penalty when the Bear coach stepped over the restraining lines.

On the Blue Monday following the game, Shaw, nettled and nervous, telephoned Sullivan and barked: "Darn it to hell, Sully. You know I didn't say any of those things."

"Yeah," replied the writer, "but you were *thinking* them!"

Four more defeats in the next six games gave the 49ers a seasonal record of 7–5 and third place in the Western Conference. The woes on the field were almost forgotten, however, when Captain Standlee was stricken by polio after the game in Los Angeles.

Everyone knew that 1952 was to be the Chief's last campaign and sorrowed with him when he broke his hand in an exhibition game and was inactive during the early spurt of victories. It was many months before Norm walked again but his recovery was complete.

Strzykalski announced that he would retire after the final game with Green Bay. A few days later Albert followed suit. Thus the careers of the three key men of the early AAC days ended within a two-week period.

Joe McTigue's 49er band played "Frankie and Johnny" as the two veterans came out of the Kezar tunnel together. They made their last appearance a good one, helping defeat the Packers, 24–14.

Despite the foldup, it had been an unforgettable year for McElhenny. The big halfback made every All-Pro team and was *Sport* magazine's "Pro Player of the Year." He had a 7-yard ground-gaining average—98 rushes for 684 yards. He caught 26 passes for 367 and ranked ninth in scoring with 60 points. His 89-yard run against Dallas was the year's longest from scrimmage. His teammates named him "The King."

It was the beginning of a great career.

CHAPTER 10

Up Again, Down Again

LOOKS LIKE BLACK YEAR FOR 49ERS!

That was the banner line in the *Chronicle* when the club opened training camp in 1953. Someone's crystal ball was hazy. It turned out to be the 49ers' best effort in the NFL— nine wins against three losses, a record usually good enough to win a championship. But Detroit was 10–2.

Fourteen spirited rookies were on the roster for the league opener at Kezar with Philadelphia. Less than 40,000 fans were in the stands, at least partly because the pre-season showing had been poor—two victories, three defeats, and a tie.

A fifteen-minute, free-swinging donnybrook with the Eagles "made" the 49ers of 1953. It was a bruising encounter from the opening kickoff, and the lid finally blew off in the third quarter, when Powell and Bobby Walston of Philadelphia traded punches. Both benches poured onto the field, and the frantic officials were practically trampled underfoot. Two Eagles singled out McElhenny; The King swung his plastic

helmet with one hand and threw punches with the other. His situation was perilous until several members of the 49er band joined the fray, using clarinets as shillelaghs.

Walter Porep, the 49er game photographer, got so interested in the proceedings he neglected to keep his cameras going. It would have been an historic film.

The fight was a draw, but the 49ers won the game, 31–21, and seemed to find a spirit that paid off all year.

They needed all of this desire the following Sunday. They trailed the Rams, 20–0, in the second quarter. Then a Los Angeles attempt to "rub it in" backfired; Van Brocklin passed instead of punting from the Ram 28-yard line on fourth down.

The 49ers were caught completely off balance and the play should have gone for a touchdown. But "Night Train" Lane, all by himself at midfield, dropped the perfect throw. Heartened, the 49ers drove in for a touchdown and it was 20–7 at the half.

They marched for another score in the third period and refused to let a Ram counter tally bother them. Lowell Wagner set up a touchdown by recovering a fumble and Rex Berry intercepted a pass to provide the points that made it 28–27 for San Francisco.

The Rams had spirit of their own and relentlessly ripped off yardage to the 49er 11, where Ben Agajanian kicked what appeared to be a winning field goal. There were three minutes to play when the 49ers huddled on their own 20 after the kickoff.

The Rams expected long, desperation passes and Tittle crossed them up. He tossed a semi-screen to McElhenny behind the line, and The King, weaving and striking like a big cobra, took advantage of a crunching block by Nomellini to run 71 yards.

While 50,000 partisans screamed and sweated, Tittle calmly

Billy Wilson and Bob St. Clair

ran out the clock for three plays. With five seconds left, he called on Soltau and the clutch artist from Minnesota provided the winning three points.

The fates had been extremely kind; now they struck the cruelest blow in 49er history.

Tittle, having his greatest year, suffered a triple fracture of the cheekbone at Detroit. The injury occurred as he fought his way into the Lion end zone early in the third period. The game was lost, 24–21, but no one could care for thinking of Y. A. in the hospital with a shattered face.

Jimmy Powers, who had sacrificed his offensive hopes to become a fine defensive back, tried valiantly to fill in at quarterback for Tittle. He was successful at Chicago as the 49ers came from behind to win, 35–28.

But the rematch with Detroit at San Francisco was disastrous, the Lions capitalizing on their only two scoring chances for a 14–10 decision.

Tittle returned wearing a mask and defied the sob sisters who said he would be gun-shy by leading the club to another triumph over the Bears.

The second game with the Rams attracted more than 90,-000 to the Memorial Coliseum, and the teams responded with another of their thrilling duels. They traded touchdowns until the Rams went ahead, 27–24, with seven minutes left. Then Tittle directed a masterful 85-yard march that was culminated by his 17-yard touchdown pass to Soltau with just a minute and twelve seconds on the clock.

After a 23–21 loss to the Browns at Cleveland, the 1953 team ran out the string with four straight victories, averaging more than 40 points per game. Perry joined the select list of players who gained more than 1,000 yards in a single season.

Joe's league-leading total was 1,018. Several weeks after the end of the season Tony called him into the office and handed him a check for $5,090—a bonus of $5 for every yard.

Rookies who had excellent years included Bob St. Clair, the six-foot-nine, 265-pound tackle; Art Michalik, middle guard; Fred Bruney, defensive back; Doug Hogland, tackle; Hal Miller, tackle; and Jack Manley, linebacker.

The enthusiasm generated by the fast finish in 1953 carried over to 1954. The club won seven exhibitions, and its display of talent was awesome. The backfield veterans included Perry, McElhenny, Schabarum, Arenas, and Billy Mixon. Down from Canada, via a trade with Pittsburgh, came John Henry Johnson.

Washington was pulverized in the opener, 41–7. Then the Tittle injury hex struck again. He got up from the turf at Los Angeles with a broken left hand and the Rams rallied for a 24–24 deadlock. His chief replacement, Arnie Galiffa, had already been shelved by the same injury in the Redskin game.

Shaw tried to use the versatile Cason at quarterback against the Packers at Milwaukee. It didn't work, and with Green

'54 49ers: Leo Nomellini standing over Art Michalik, Hardy Brown, Billy Mixon and Nick Feher

Bay leading in the fourth period, Tittle, wearing a special cast designed by Dr. Bill O'Grady, went in and salvaged a 23–17 victory.

At Chicago, Tittle was in obvious distress during the first half, which found the Bears taking a 21–7 lead. Buck called on Maury Duncan, a virtually unknown rookie quarterback, and the youngster was equal to the occasion. Long runs by Perry and McElhenny saved the day, 31–24.

Detroit was edged at Kezar, 37–31, but it was another costly afternoon. Cason and Berry, the heart of the defensive secondary, were injured and lost for most of the remaining contests.

The old devil Bears came to the Golden Gate, and the sad story of 1952 was repeated. A rookie end, Harlon Hill, caught four touchdown passes, the last with only twenty-five seconds remaining, and the bubble burst again, 27–31. Worst of all, McElhenny suffered a shoulder separation and was out for the

John Henry Johnson loose for yardage against the Bears

year. He was running wild in the league at the time with 64 carries for 515 yards, an amazing 8-yard average.

When the club dropped successive games to Los Angeles and Detroit—the latter a 48–7 pasting that was the worst of Shaw's coaching career—reporters began calling Tony about Buck's future.

The answer was: "No comment."

It was an infuriating reply to many of the newspapermen, who were either rehiring or firing Shaw in print. They wanted corroboration, either way, for their opinions.

They overlooked part of 49er tradition: the management left the coaches on their own after training camp opened. The summing up was withheld until the end of each season.

Tony couldn't say what would happen in Buck's case because he didn't know himself. He had to weigh all the arguments carefully before making a decision after the last game.

The pro-Shaw factions, and they were legion, pointed to the

injuries that had crippled his better clubs. They said the type of football he coached had made the 49ers the best-drawing club on the road in the league in 1952–53–54—a statement of fact—and that his players swore by him.

The critics argued that Shaw had gone nine years without winning any kind of a championship, a far longer time than usually allowed a professional or major college coach. They declared he had full authority in drafting players and should have had "bench strength" to protect against injuries.

"He's too easy on the players," they added. "He won't discipline anyone for anything short of murder."

In the end, Tony made the generally unpopular decision— he notified Buck his contract would not be renewed.

CHAPTER 11

The Great Newspaper Feud and Other Phenomena

BY the end of the Shaw era, Tony Morabito's feuds with certain sports writers had become a much-discussed topic, especially when newspapermen gathered. The talk contained some fact and a lot of fiction.

Paradoxically, Tony's celebrated battle with the San Francisco *Examiner* began because he would not break a pledge he had given the city's other three newspapers. He had received warm support and encouragement from Bill Leiser, sports editor of the *Chronicle,* when he first began planning major league professional football for San Francisco. Bud Spencer of the *News* and Ernie Cope and Jack McDonald of the *Call-Bulletin* also favored the project in their columns. *Examiner* writers listed pro ball as of dubious value to the city and did not believe it would catch on with the public.

In his innocence, Tony was delighted when *Examiner* offi-

cials suddenly proposed that the 49ers play an annual exhibition game for the paper's charity fund.

"This is great," he told friends. "Now we'll have all the
papers backing pro ball."

He signed a five-year contract.

The other sports editors were bewildered—and hurt.

"We've supported you from the beginning," they said, "and
now you're signed up with the *Examiner*."

"Gentlemen, I've made a mistake," he said. "I can only
promise you that when the five years are up, the 49ers will
play this charity game for all the papers."

The last year of the contract, 1950, was marked by the
49ers' entrance into the NFL and the *Examiner* asked for a
new ten-year pact. Tony explained his position and suggested
the game for all the papers. The answer was a definite no.

From then on, Tony and his brother, Vic, were subjected
to a campaign of vilification that has had few parallels in
sports. Tony was referred to as "You Gotta Be Hard Morabito" and he was pictured as a penny-pinching skinflint who
hired football players at starvation wages. (Note: In 1957,
records of the Congressional committee investigating professional sports showed that for the five preceding years the 49ers
had been among the four top-salaried clubs in the NFL. In
1958, Vic Morabito said publicly that the club, that year, had
the highest payroll in the league—and the statement was not
challenged.)

Friends warned Tony that he "couldn't fight a newspaper."
They declared it was "bad business."

"This is a matter of principle, not business," he said.

Forty-Niner news was buried on back pages in 1950, but
as pro interest steadily grew in San Francisco, coverage in the
Examiner increased.

The all-time journalistic low was reached in 1956, however, when Curley Grieve inferred in his column that Red

Strader's fatal heart attack was brought on by his firing as 49er head coach. After that column, Tony refused to take an *Examiner* writer along on 49er road trips—at the club's expense—and the paper's representatives were barred from training camp quarters and press conferences. They were not barred from the dressing room after games.

In February of 1958, an official of another Hearst newspaper told Vic Morabito he had been assigned to "mediate" the disagreement.

"Will you sit down with the publisher and sports editor of the *Examiner* and get this thing straightened out?" the official asked Vic.

The younger Morabito agreed and was told that a meeting would be arranged for the following week. After waiting in vain for a call, the 49ers could only surmise that the mediator failed to gain the co-operation of his own organization.

Tony was to find that among writers on other papers the merits of his case were lost in the general journalistic tradition of sticking together. Criticism was heaped on him from other sources.

Will Connolly of the *Chronicle* wrote that NFL owners were "interested only in blood and shoulder separations." Tony protested this vigorously and relations with the *Chronicle* were impaired for several seasons. Minor brush fires flared, died, and broke out again.

He honestly hated to see his name in the papers, but he couldn't help making news. After he died they called him "colorful."

During all this turmoil, the 49ers were establishing season ticket sales records almost every year. From 4,448 in 1951, the sales jumped to 9,486 in 1954. When Shaw was fired, several "oracles"—"oracle" being Tony's epithet for a writer who opposed him—predicted the club would lose thousands of season ticket buyers. Instead, the total jumped almost 100 per cent to 16,244.

By 1957, it was 20,737. Then came the unbelievable increase to 38,400 in 1958.

And Tony was the best friend the public ever had when it came to buying tickets. It was "first come, first served," and companies and celebrities who neglected to get in line early found that no choice locations had been held back to accommodate them.

Franklin Mieuli, who bought a 10 per cent interest in the club in 1954, well remembers his ticket initiation.

"After we signed the papers," Mieuli recalls, "I told Tony I was interested in getting some good season seats for myself, my parents and close business associates. I had visions of at least ten right on the fifty-yard line.

"Tony said, 'Fine, come with me.' He took me out to the ticket office where there were five or six people standing in line. We waited in line. When we got up to the counter, he introduced me to Wanda Murray, the assistant season ticket director.

" 'Show Mr. Mieuli what you have available,' he told Wanda. She had large charts on which every location was marked. I meekly picked out ten around the twenty-yard line. I wasn't very happy about it then, but those seats are like gold now."

(Kezar, with its 59,000 capacity, has only 19,000 seats between the goal lines, and there are unhappy wails every year from fans who purchased season books after 1956 and have been unable to improve their locations. Several times ticket director Peter Giannini has been forced to referee for divorcing couples who claim custody of choice seats.)

CHAPTER 12

Strader Lasts Quick

PERSONS inside, as well as outside, the 49er organization were surprised when Norman P. (Red) Strader was named to succeed Buck Shaw as head coach.

Tony Morabito and Red had not been friendly when the latter was with the New York Yankees during the All-America Conference years. They became cold in 1950 when Tony accused Red of having one of his former Yankee players scout the 49ers in practice.

Red had been a great athlete at St. Mary's College. In 1924 he became the school's first football player to receive All-America recognition from Walter Camp. After a playing career in both professional football and baseball, Strader coached at Regis College in Denver, then returned to St. Mary's as chief assistant to "Slip" Madigan in 1932.

He succeeded Madigan as head coach in 1939 and later spent four years in the Navy as an athletic officer and administrator. He joined the Yankees as backfield coach in 1946 and stepped into the top job in 1948 when Ray Flaherty was dismissed.

After one season with the Yanks in the NFL, Red had contract trouble with owner Ted Collins and decided to go into the construction business in the San Francisco area.

Strader was breezy, fast-talking—the direct opposite of Shaw. The difference carried over into their coaching methods. Red believed in organizing down to the last detail. He was determined that under his regime the 49ers would no longer be known as the "country club of the National League"—a tag hung on them several years previously by a famous owner and coach.

For assistants, Strader picked Howard (Red) Hickey, who had resigned as a Ram assistant after fourteen years as player and coach with that organization; Phil Bengtson, a holdover from the Shaw era; Mark Duncan of Colorado A&M; and Frankie Albert.

No 49er team ever came into training camp in better condition than the 1955 group. The veterans were worried, to put it mildly, that they wouldn't fit into Strader's plans.

After a few weeks of training at St. Mary's College in Moraga Valley, there was an undercurrent of grumbling.

"We're being led around by the hand like a bunch of children," a veteran said. "This minute-by-minute schedule every day makes me feel as though I'm in military school."

Red patrolled the halls of the dormitory every night from 10:30 to 11 P.M., personally making sure everyone was in his room. Someone added to the grimness of the atmosphere by playing taps on a bungle in an upstairs corridor.

The general unrest increased when McElhenny hurt his foot in a pre-season game with Pittsburgh. It didn't seem serious at first, but the injury failed to respond to treatment. In desperation, the club sent The King to specialists at Johns Hopkins in Baltimore, and they could not find the answer either.

It was finally determined that the injury was related to a

mishap when McElhenny was eleven years old. He cut his foot on a broken bottle and was on crutches for almost a year.

McElhenny was in the line-up often during the regular season, carrying the ball ninety times. But he gained only 327 yards for a 3.6 average, by far the poorest of his career. He literally played on one leg.

It was a frustrating season from start to finish. Typical of it was the game at Washington, when the 49ers had three touchdowns called back and suffered the ignominy of a shutout at the hands of the Redskins. By the end of the schedule, Red, driving himself mercilessly, was going in one direction and the squad in another. The final record was four wins and eight losses. Red met with the owners for a review of the situation. He was asked if the seasonal record was indicative of 49er personnel.

"Absolutely," he replied. "In fact, I'd say we were lucky to win four games."

The statement was directly contrary to his assessment of the squad in September, even after McElhenny was injured. This, plus the knowledge that the players had come close to open revolt, settled the issue. A press conference was called, and Red's dismissal announced. "Incompatibility between the head coach and the players," was the way Tony put it.

Ten days later Tony staggered the football world again by naming Frank Albert head coach.

Albert's coaching experience was limited to a couple of spring practices at Stanford and the Naval Academy, plus his brief association with Strader, during which he was mainly responsible for filing the information sent in by 49er talent scouts.

Frank kept the same corps of assistants and added Bill (Tiger) Johnson, long-time 49er center and one of the most underrated players in pro football.

Tittle diving for score in 30–17 upset of Baltimore

Jack McDonald of the *Call-Bulletin* visited training camp at St. Mary's in August of 1956 and wrote:

When Albert got the 49er job, even his friends feared his dislike of practice routine might be his undoing. Small details were not his style. Only the grand strategy appealed to him. But the sun hadn't yet sunk behind the Moraga hills after the first practice when those who had him pegged as a "no detail" man knew they were wrong. The place reeked, but not unpleasantly, with organization. He had mapped specific, sensible work schedules months ago and they were followed almost on the split second. Things went off like clockwork. Assistants and players knew what was expected and Frankie gave them their heads.

The club won three straight exhibition games from the champion Browns, Redskins and Cardinals. Albert, at thirty-six the youngest head coach in the league, was naturally hailed as the "Boy Wonder." Just as rapidly, the 49ers dropped three pre-season engagements to the Giants, Rams, and Eagles. Now Albert was criticized for trading such veterans as end Clay Matthews and tackle Marion Campbell, both to Philadelphia; guard Doug Hogland to the Cardinals, and halfback Fred Bruney to Pittsburgh.

The outlook was so serious that "Tiger" Johnson was persuaded to "unretire" and resume his duties at offensive center. Even his presence on the field couldn't stem a 38–21 thumping by the Giants in the league opener.

The skies cleared briefly when the Rams were shaded, 33–30, mainly because of five fumble recoveries and four field goals by Soltau. The respite was brief—five straight defeats gave the 49ers a 1–6 record when they arrived at Green Bay November 18 for the final game of all time in historic City Stadium.

Tittle, who had been displaced temporarily as the starting quarterback by Earl Morrall, rookie from Michigan State, finally returned to the field and the 49ers won, 17–16. McElhenny's 86-yard touchdown run was the turning point.

Three players picked up on waivers from other clubs provided a spark for the stretch drive. They were Bobby Holladay, defensive halfback from Los Angeles; J. D. Smith, defensive halfback from the Chicago Bears, and Stan Sheriff, linebacker from Pittsburgh.

The 49ers won a 10–10 deadlock at Philadelphia by holding the Eagles on the one-yard line as the game ended. A 77-yard pass play from Tittle to Wilson, with Billy hurdling three Colt tacklers, gained an uphill 20–17 victory at Baltimore.

Wins over the Packers, 38–20, and the Colts again, 30–17, closed out what had become an unexpectedly respectable season. In the final game, Arenas had one of his greatest afternoons, returning a kickoff 96 yards and a punt 67.

The 5–6–1 showing was good enough for third place in the Western Conference behind the Bears and Dertoit.

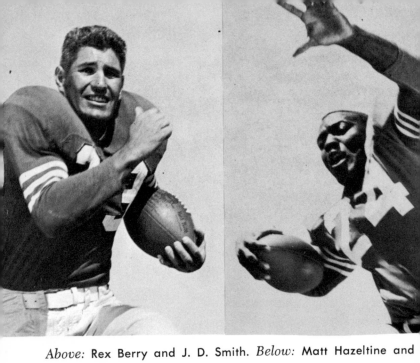

Above: Rex Berry and J. D. Smith. *Below:* Matt Hazeltine and R. C. Owens

CHAPTER 13

The Cliff-Hangers of 1957

IF a Hollywood scenario writer had written the script for the 49er season of 1957, he would be led to the nearest psychiatrist. Off the field as well as on, the season was packed with every heartthrob and accident known to soap opera.

This was a 49er squad that did not compare in personnel to several of its predecessors. There were definite weaknesses in the offensive line and defensive backfield. But the club had a flaming spirit and found a powerful reason to succeed. The players battled uphill against heavy odds in almost every game. They lived by the sword of miraculous comebacks; in the end, they perished in the same manner when Detroit defeated them in the Western Conference play-off.

During the off season, Albert traded Henry Johnson to Detroit for Bill Stits. The critics howled that the Lions got much the better of the deal. As far as "names" were concerned they did; yet it was apparent to most fans that John Henry for two years had failed to approach his rookie performance, while Stits was a steady defensive halfback.

The club defeated the champion Giants, Washington, and Cleveland in home exhibition games, then went to Seattle and overcame a two-touchdown deficit in the fourth quarter to beat the Chicago Cardinals, 27–21. Spectators went home talking about a "circus" catch made by R. C. Owens, a six-foot-three, 207-pound rookie end from College of Idaho.

Owens leaped high into the air in the Cardinal end zone to snatch a seemingly wild pass from Tittle for a touchdown. Until that afternoon Owens was just another obscure newcomer. His three catches for 109 yards cinched a regular season job.

The club appeared to have a scoring punch; that the defensive problems were far from settled became apparent when the Rams gained 580 yards passing and running in piling up a 58–27 exhibition victory at Los Angeles.

Albert's head was hanging low in the locker room, and Tony tried to comfort him.

"We've got to get a linebacker," Frank said.

"If you're willing to give up a couple of good ballplayers, I think I know where we can get one," Tony replied.

The next morning the 49er owner put in a call for Buddy Parker, the Pittsburgh coach. The Steelers were in dire need of a quarterback. The 49ers had three in Tittle, Morrall and John Brodie, rookie from Stanford.

"How'd you like to have Morrall?" Tony asked Parker.

Buddy was unable to restrain his enthusiasm—a dangerous attitude when trades are discussed. He screamed in anguish, however, when Tony named Marv Matuszak, the Steeler linebacker, as the player the 49ers wanted, plus Pittsburgh's first-draft choice for two years.

Parker was on the spot—no pro club can function without a first-class quarterback. He finally demanded Mike Sandusky, a promising rookie guard, along with Morrall. Sold!

Matuszak's aggressiveness and leadership on defense became apparent the following week when Philadelphia was defeated in the final pre-season game.

The team, shaken by the thrashing in Los Angeles, grew confident during preparations for the first league game with the Cardinals. Albert, thinking out loud as he was wont to do, told Walt Daley of the *Call-Bulletin:*

"We should beat the Cardinals. We're going to be in plenty of trouble if we don't."

In general, he meant that the Western Conference of the NFL was regarded as stronger than the Eastern Conference, and the Cardinals were not rated highly in the latter division.

Coach Ray Richards of the Cardinals, of course, used the quotation as a rallying cry for his players and their attitude at kickoff time was menacing. Ollie Matson, enjoying his first good afternoon at Kezar against the 49ers, returned the first punt of the game 28 yards, then passed to Dave Mann for 32 yards to set up a touchdown.

A 35-yard field goal by Soltau and a 90-yard touchdown drive, featured by McElhenny's 61-yard run, gave the 49ers a 10–7 lead. Matson and Johnny Olszewski spurred a Cardinal resurgence that finished with Joe Childress going down the middle 39 yards to the end zone. Pat Summerall added field goals in the third and fourth periods for a final score of 20–10. In the game, Larry Barnes, rookie fullback from Colorado A&M, set an all-time 49er record with a punt of 86 yards.

Morale was low when the 49ers assembled at Redwood City Tuesday to begin work for a meeting with the Rams. If they couldn't beat the "weak" Cardinals, how could they be expected to stop the talent-laden Los Angeles team?

The last part of the afternoon was devoted to a dummy scrimmage on pass plays. The passers had trouble finding targets; when they did, the receivers usually dropped the ball. Tittle, finding himself pressured by incoming linemen, finally flung the ball away as if in disgust.

Above: Charlie Powell (87) comes up fast to help down Rams' Waller. *Below:* 49er defense closes in on Leon Clarke after 70-yard pass-and-run from Van Brockin

(Both photos courtesy Frank Rippon)

It looked like one of Rip Sewell's "blooper" pitches for the Pittsburgh Pirates. The ball seemed to hang in the sky, then floated down to where Owens stood amid three defensive backs. Suddenly, the former basketball star leaped into the air and grabbed the pigskin as the defenders stood open-mouthed.

The incident seemed to take the edge off the gloom and wheels started turning in Red Hickey's head.

"Hey, that's our 'Alley-Oop' play!" he shouted.

The rest of the week, the unorthodox maneuver was practiced ten to fifteen minutes daily. Still, the coaches thought of it more as a tonic for the team's morale than as a regular play in the repertoire.

On Sunday 59,637 people, the first of six straight home sellouts, inundated Kezar. Their main hope was for a respectable 49er showing. Even this dream flickered in the first five minutes when the Rams took advantage of a short 49er punt to launch a march from their own 45. Tom Wilson went around end for 21 yards to score without anyone touching him.

The 49ers dug in. They were handed two points early in the second period when Tom Wilson, forced into the end zone by a bad pitchout, was tackled by Nomellini. Arenas returned Norm Van Brocklin's free kick 21 yards to the Ram 45. On second down, Tittle passed over the middle to Clyde Conner, who lateraled to Billy Wilson on the 23. Billy went all the way, and it was 9-7.

A Ram score was averted when J. D. Smith fell on an end-zone fumble for a touchback. With about three minutes to play in the half, the 49ers started from their own 20, struggling as far as the Ram 46 with fifty seconds on the clock. Tittle dropped back and aimed the ball at the corner of the end zone. Owens and Don Burroughs raced step for step, and both got their hands on leather. But R. C. came up with the prize.

After the second-half kickoff, Van Brocklin and Leon Clarke collaborated on a typical Ram "bomb"—a 70-yard pass-run play for a touchdown. Two field goals by Paige Cothren sent the Rams into a 20–16 lead with eleven minutes to go.

A 38-yard kickoff returned by J. D. Smith, embellished by hard line plunging by McElhenny and Gene Babb, a rookie in for Perry at fullback, advanced the 49ers to the Los Angeles 11. On second down, Tittle stepped into the huddle and said: "We'll go for the Alley-Oop!"

It was almost simple. Owens ran over the goal line and stood alongside Jesse Castete. Tittle threw the blooper, and R. C. sprang at exactly the right moment. The 23–20 score stood up during the ensuing three minutes and fifteen seconds .

With Perry still ailing, Babb had to assume the fullback role and acquitted himself admirably in a bruising match with the Bears at Chicago. The first half was scoreless. A Bear threat was snuffed out when Matuszak recovered Bobby Watkins' fumble on the San Francisco 2-yard line. The 49ers got to the Bear 6 in the second period, but Babb dropped the ball and J. C. Caroline flopped on it.

The Bears, riding on the punishing blasts of Rick Casares, scored in the third period after recovering McElhenny's fumble on the 49er 33. Tittle got those points back on two passes—40 yards to Wilson and 30 to Owens.

The 49ers pushed ahead on one of their old standbys— Tittle pitched out to Arenas, who faked a run and then passed 33 yards to Clyde Conner. A 39-yard pass from Ed Brown to Harlon Hill, followed by Casares' touchdown plunge, and George Blanda's 17-yard field goal gave Chicago a 17–14 margin with 4:29 to play.

When Bill George threw Tittle for a 12-yard loss and forced the 49ers to punt, the cause seemed hopeless. But Ed Henke and Charlie Powell checked the Bears with fine defensive efforts, and Brown had to kick. Arenas fought his way out of bounds on the 43.

Tittle, dueling the clock, threw a screen to McElhenny for 26 yards. An Alley Oop to Owens was incomplete in the end zone. Conner took a pass for 12, but a second was over his head. Then Wilson, the hook artist, faked into the clear; Tittle hit him for 12.

As the ball was snapped for the next play, Owens was knocked down at the line of scrimmage, the Bears' 7. He crawled into the end zone on his hands and knees and was in that position when Tittle, almost blanketed by frantic Bears, shot the ball low and hard into his hands. Twenty-seven seconds later the game ended. The score—49ers 21, Bears 17.

"I call that my 'prayer pass,' " R. C. said later.

The 49ers looked like anything except title contenders at Milwaukee but managed to stumble past the Packers, 24–14. They headed home for the crucial rematch with the aroused Bears, several of whom had been quoted as saying the 49ers were the "worst team we've played all year."

This was the last week of Tony Morabito's life—and it was a happy one. He spent Tuesday at practice, congratulating each player individually for the memorable victory at Wrigley Field.

The hero behind the scenes that week was Dr. James O'Connor, associate team physician. Several players had been hit by influenza before the Packer game; now the ailment became almost epidemic, and eight men were unable to practice Friday morning. Day and night Dr. Jim made his house calls.

"I'll have them ready Sunday," he vowed, "but only the good Lord knows how long they'll last."

Greeted by another screaming capacity crowd, the 49ers were overeager in the first quarter. They fumbled the opening kickoff and the Bears scored in three plays. A 53-yard pass from Brown to Hill soon led to a second touchdown, and now the crowd was as silent as the gray fog that crept in from the ocean.

After he had been thrown for a 14-yard loss, Tittle called time and lectured his teammates. "We can play better ball than this! For crying out loud, calm down and start blocking!"

His rare outburst was effective. Arenas returned a punt 18 yards; plunges by Babb, interspersed with passes to Wilson and Conner, took the ball to the Bear one; and Y. A. sneaked it across.

Then, as the 49er defense stiffened and threw the Bears back, Tony suffered his fatal collapse. The players learned of it when they went off the field trailing, 17–7 (Blanda had kicked a 26-yard field goal just as the half ended).

Midway in the third period, Dr. Bill O'Grady brought the dreaded news from the hospital. There was a moment of stunned silence, then the bench became a madhouse of crying, shouting players.

The Bears were pushed back to their 23, and Brown punted. But he was roughed by several wild men, and given a new chance by the penalty, the Chicagoans advanced the ball to the San Francisco 38. There Powell charged in and dropped Willie Galimore for an 11-yard loss.

Nomellini, tears streaming down his face, savagely rushed Brown on an attempted pass. The ball was picked off by Bill Herchman on the 49er 46-yard line, and the big tackle, convoyed by Bob Toneff, went all the way.

As the last period began, Brown's pass was deflected by Matuszak and intercepted by Dick Moegle, who dodged and twisted for 40 yards. Perry, who had pleaded to get into the game despite his knee injury, boomed into the line and gained 8 yards with Bears hanging all over him. Tittle, fading back from the Chicago 11, found Wilson clear in the right flat and passed to him for the winning touchdown—again, 21–17.

There were still more than twelve minutes to play and in that time the Bears had the ball for twenty-five plays against nine for the 49ers. The officials penalized San Francisco for roughing the passer, clipping, a personal foul, and pass interference.

J. D. Smith stopped one drive with an interception on the one-yard line. Just before the gun, the Bears reached the 13, and Zeke Bratkowski tried to hit Hill in the end zone. But Moegle, playing his greatest game as a 49er, made his third interception of the day and returned 29 yards.

Ed Henke, who had given every ounce of his energy, collapsed from sheer exhaustion as Tittle held the ball on the final play.

Jack McDonald described in the *Call-Bulletin* the scene after the game:

It was the same dressing room into which Tony had strode, in good spirits, just half an hour before the game, pumping everybody's hand and telling each the Bears could be beat. The last player he had talked to was Charlie Powell. "Now, Charlie," he had said, "don't let those Bears get you mad and make you do something you'll regret." . . . With that Tony had left the dressing room and made arrangements for his godson, 13-year-old Steve Ruffo, to sit on the 49er bench during the game.

The genuine grief felt for Morabito was a testimonial to the high regard his players had for the man. Big Leo Nomellini wept a stream of unashamed tears. Most of the players sobbed audibly. Albert cried out in anguish: "I'd rather have lost this game by 100 points than to lose Tony."

Joe Perry said: "For nine years I signed blank contracts with him. I knew he'd fill in a more than fair salary figure. Many people don't know the nice things he's done. He didn't want them told, but I know lots of wonderful things about him."

And Tittle, his voice choking, said, "He was always fair and honest. I never had to read my contract for any fine print. His word was his bond. Any player with financial or other worries could always go to Tony."

Gordy Soltau remembered that when the NFL players formed their association in 1956, a move that was fought by some of the more powerful owners, Tony called the 49ers together.

"He told us that if we thought we could better ourselves by forming the association, he'd stand behind us," Soltau said. "More than that, he paid the expenses of the 49er who represented our players at the first association meeting in Philadelphia."

But for all the tributes and sorrow, next Sunday came, and so did Detroit. The Lions jumped into a 10–0 lead; the 49ers, with Tittle on the beam, countered with two touchdowns and led at the intermission, 14–10. They stretched this to 28–10 early in the fourth period. Then Tobin Rote replaced Bobby Layne at quarterback and set the Lions on fire. He threw three touchdown passes—two to Jim Doran and one to Steve Junker—the third coming with a minute and twenty seconds to play to give the Lions a 31–28 advantage.

Disappointed fans began leaving the stands. The 49ers already had received more than their share of miracles.

Arenas returned the kickoff from the end zone to the 28-yard line. There were sixty seconds left.

Tittle passed to Babb for one, Wilson for 12, McElhenny for 10 and again for 8. The King bulled his way out of bounds to stop the clock with nineteen seconds left, and now the fans were standing and screaming. The 49ers ran out of their huddle to start the play on the Detroit 41.

The Lions used only a four-man rush but still managed to

Lincoln Kimura, Bill Herchman (*back turned*), Billy Kim, Coach
Frank Albert, and Clyde Connor as R. C. Owens catches a 41-yard
"Alley-Oop" from Y. A. Tittle to beat Detroit

break through. Tittle ran for his life to his right, and Owens
meanwhile was loping to the goal line, covered every inch of
the way by Jim David. As the ball climbed into the dark sky,
scattering a flock of shrieking sea gulls, Jack Christiansen, another Detroit defensive back, raced over to assist David.

The ball slowly spiraled down toward the two white shirts
and the one cardinal jersey just inside the end zone. Timing
his leap to perfection, Owens clutched the ball in big hands
and fell to the ground between the outraged defenders.

The 35–31 win gave the 49ers a 5–1 mark and a two-game
lead in the Western Conference with six games remaining.
Mailbags bulging with championship game orders arrived at
the office. Each order had to be returned. A grim four-game
road trip lay ahead; and the club had come a cropper on the
road all too often.

At Los Angeles, 102,368 people—the largest crowd in pro

football history—pushed through the turnstiles at Memorial Coliseum. An estimated 10,000 would-be ticket purchasers were turned away.

The Rams dominated the game all the way and won, 37–24. There was sorrow but no panic among the 49ers. The panic came next week, when Detroit scored 21 points in the second quarter and went on to dominate San Francisco, 31–10, before a capacity crowd at Briggs Stadium.

Now the 49ers, tied with the Lions and Colts at 5–3, had to face the unfriendly, roaring mob at Baltimore. It was a bitter dogfight for sixty minutes. After a 14–14 first half, the Colts forged ahead, 20–14, in the third period on two field goals by Steve Myrha.

Tittle's passes to Owens, Babb, and Wilson kept the 49ers alive, and Y. A. bulled over from the one-yard line. Soltau's conversion made it 21–20 with three minutes to play. Ray Berry saved the Colts on third down on their own 46-yard line with an impossible catch of a 31-yard aerial from Johnny Unitas. With fifty-three seconds to play, Unitas passed 8 yards to Alan Ameche for the winning touchdown—27–21.

In an effort to chase the blues, Albert gave the players Monday off in New York. On Tuesday morning the 49ers bused up to Bear Mountain Inn and started work for their do-or-die game with the Giants, who were battling Cleveland for first place in the Eastern Conference.

The dark and dreary days were brightened only by the arrival of Bob (The Geek) St. Clair, the big tackle who had been sidelined with a shoulder separation.

The Geek walked into the lobby of the inn, dropped his suitcase on the floor, drew himself up to his full six feet nine inches and announced to the openmouthed guests: "I am Moses, come to lead the 49ers out of the wilderness!"

Albert made an important defensive move, putting Karl Rubke, a tall, rawboned rookie from Southern California, at middle linebacker and switching Matuszak to the left side and Matt Hazeltine to the right.

There was snow on the ground at Yankee Stadium and the temperature was in the low 20's, but the 49ers were "hot" for the first time in a month. The Giants had been inclined to look past the faltering San Franciscans to their divisional climax with Cleveland.

The result was a 27–17 upset. Credit belonged equally to a revitalized offense, with St. Clair giving the backs running room, and a ball-hawking defense, inspired by Rubke, Henke, Hazeltine, Herchman, and Nomellini. The Giants lost the ball six times on fumbles. Tittle, putting on a show for the New York writers, clinched his "Player of the Year" award by completing 11 of 16 passes for 143 yards and running five times for 49 vital yards.

When the team arrived at San Francisco International Airport at 3 A.M., hundreds of fans were on hand. Tittle was limping from a pulled leg muscle but promised, in an impromptu speech, that he would be ready for the rematch with the Colts.

All reserved seats for the game had been sold out for several weeks. Five thousand general admission tickets were to go on sale Sunday at 9 A.M., but fans started lining up at 4 P.M. Saturday. It was a bitter cold night; heavy clothing—and warming spirits—were very much in evidence.

The long lines, snaking back into Golden Gate Park, were relatively calm until the ticket sellers, escorted by a police squad, entered the booths. Then the crowd surged forward; crashers added to the confusion by attempting to get into the lines from the side. One of the booths teetered on its foundations, and two terrified ticket sellers crouched inside and screamed for help.

Mounted policemen undoubtedly saved several lives when they urged their horses through the milling mob, up to the booth. Four men were arrested for disturbing the peace, and the sale of tickets resumed. They were gone within an hour.

Lou Spadia, 49er general manager, was left sweating profusely. He said: "The day of the horse is not gone. If it hadn't been for those mounted police, blood would have been shed here."

The game lived up to its billing as a struggle for first place. The Colts were called for pass interference on McElhenny on the one-yard line, and the 49ers scored first. Baltimore tied it up when Milt Davis picked off a Tittle throw and ran 75 yards. Nomellini blocked the conversion. Before the half, Soltau raised the difference with a 16-yard field goal.

In the third quarter, Lenny Moore got behind the 49er secondary, and Unitas reached him with an arching pass. The play was good for 72 yards and Baltimore led, 13–10.

Tittle was taking a terrific pounding from the Colt forwards—he lost 52 yards during the afternoon—and the 49ers couldn't seem to put a drive together. But with a minute and fifteen seconds left to play, McElhenny took a short pass over the middle, eluded two tacklers, and ghosted 43 yards through a broken field until he was ridden out of bounds on the Baltimore 15.

A swing pass to Perry gained only a yard. On second down, Tittle was swarmed under and passed wildly over the end zone. The veteran quarterback couldn't pull himself off the ground, and the crowd groaned.

Two teammates carried Y. A. to the bench, and Brodie came in. It was a brutal spot for a rookie who had played only a few minutes during the season. John, a self-confident youngster, was probably the coolest person in the stadium.

His first pass, intended for Wilson, was incomplete. Then John, chased by a half ton of Colt fury, dropped back and looked for McElhenny. The King drove straight into the end zone and cut sharply to his left. The ball shot in shoulder-high and The King grabbed it—17–13. There was time for only one play after the kickoff.

Trainer Henry Schmidt, under the direction of Drs. O'Grady and O'Connor, worked feverishly all week on Tittle's ailing legs. The "Bald Eagle's" health was the main concern of the press, but the new legion of Brodie admirers were positive he could direct the team to a win over Green Bay in the final game. The Packers, their ranks thinned by injuries, were a 14-point underdog.

With Tittle still hobbling, Brodie got the starting assignment and piloted the 49ers into a 10–0 first-quarter lead. The Packers refused to quit. Bart Starr's accurate passes pulled them into a 20–10 half-time advantage.

When Tittle, gimpy legs and all, ran onto the field after the second-half kickoff, the crowd went hysterical. Y. A. directed a drive that stuttered on the Packer 28, but Soltau kicked a field goal for 20–13.

The aroused 49ers beat the Packers back, and Val Joe Walker returned an intercepted pass from the visitors' 30 to the 12. Perry scored in two plays and Soltau's conversion tied it up. Tittle's passing and Perry's running produced a 69-yard 49er parade for the winning touchdown.

A few minutes after the game ended, the 49ers learned the Rams had upset the Colts, 37–21. Detroit, meanwhile, had downed the Bears, 21–13, to gain a play-off with San Francisco.

On Sunday, December 22, 1957, the script went awry. San Francisco, now famous for fantastic comebacks, was itself the victim of a Detroit club that refused to throw in the sponge when it trailed, 27–7, in the third quarter.

The 49ers' first touchdown came early in the game on the Alley-Oop—a 34-yarder from Tittle to Owens. Then McElhenny took a pass over the middle and pounded 47 yards for a second score. Wilson contributed one of his patented circus catches for the third touchdown, and Soltau added a 25-yard field goal for a 24–7 half-time rout.

On the first play of the second half, McElhenny accepted a pitchout, hesitated for a key block by Lou Palatella, and swerved 71 yards to the Detroit 9-yard line before he was dragged out of bounds. But here the Lions, led by Joe Schmidt, their great linebacker, held firm and the 49ers had to settle for Soltau's field goal.

This was to be the high-water mark in 49er history. From this pinnacle the San Franciscans were repelled by a suddenly potent Detroit offense and defense. Tobin Rote couldn't miss his receivers; Tom Tracy, a third-string fullback, ran straight down the middle for 58 yards and a touchdown; the 49ers were forced into unmentionable sins of omission and commission.

Detroit, fated to go on and annihilate Cleveland in the championship game, shaded the 49ers, 31 to 27.

CHAPTER **14**

Hickey for Albert

AT the beginning of the 1958 NFL season, head coach Frank Albert was still cocky and boyish-looking. Three months later there were streaks of gray in his dark brown hair, pouches of worry under his eyes, and lines in his face. When he saw the change in a mirror he handed in his resignation to Vic Morabito.

Football had been fun and frolic to Frank when he was a player. His carefree attitude carried over into the deadly serious business of coaching; undoubtedly it was a prime factor in the comeback of 1956 and the highly successful campaign in 1957.

But Frank, like most extroverts, had an extremely sensitive side. His pride was crushed when the Rams humbled the 49ers, 33–3, in the second league game at San Francisco, and his world practically fell apart when his team took a horrible 56–7 beating at Los Angeles.

He had always been a fighter, but there was no way to de-

Lynn Waldorf regales 49er training camp with his famous limericks. Front-row audience includes Frank Albert, Eddie Forest, Jesse Freitas, Bob Tichenal, Bob Toneff, Dick Moegle

fend against unkind remarks directed at members of his family after the holocaust in the Memorial Coliseum. Other coaches before him had endured abuse themselves but wilted when it was hurled at their wives and children.

Frank was blamed in some quarters for making Brodie the No. 1 quarterback when the regular season began. Critics agreed that Tittle had not been effective in the exhibition games but pointed out that he had had brief slumps before and always managed to snap out of them when the chips were down.

In truth, the Tittle-Brodie controversy had been debated endlessly by the entire coaching staff, and the younger quarterback got the majority vote.

The 49ers opened in typical cliff-hanger fashion, nosing out

Pittsburgh, 23–20. Three interceptions by Bill Stits and Soltau's 22-yard field goal in the last three minutes thwarted the Steelers.

Next week they took that thrashing by the Rams, so Tittle was nominated to start against the Bears at Chicago. He suffered a groin injury and the 49ers took another lacing, 28–6. Brodie motored the team to a 30–24 decision over the Eagles at Philadelphia.

Another loss to the Bears—27–14 at San Francisco—was followed by a 24–21 upset victory over Detroit. Against the Lions Perry increased his all-time ground gaining record with 174 yards on 13 attempts, and McElhenny scored the winning touchdown on a 32-yard run that actually covered three times that distance.

Then came Los Angeles. There were 95,000 people in the Coliseum, and it seemed to Frank Albert that all of them were chanting for the Rams to pour it on. They did. They made their last touchdown, for a total of 56 points, with one second to play.

The sad tale was almost repeated at Detroit. The Lions rolled up a 28–7 lead at the half. The groggy 49ers finally regained their punch, albeit too late. Detroit, 35; San Francisco, 21.

It was after the Detroit game that Albert went to Vic Morabito and told him he was planning to resign at the end of the season.

"Think it over carefully, Frank," cautioned Vic. "There're still four games to go."

There was no need to discuss contract technicalities. Frank's "contract" with both Tony and Vic was a handshake.

The squad knew something was in the air and next Sunday responded with supercharged performances. The 49ers scored 21 points in the fourth period to defeat Green Bay, 33–12. But the following week the Colts, behind by 20 points after two periods, came on to win, 35–27, and clinch their first division title.

Back home, the 49ers handled Green Bay, 48–21. And then Albert's coaching career—his decision to resign was announced two days before the game—closed on a high note with a 21–12 upset of the Colts.

As generally expected, Howard Wayne (Red) Hickey was named to succeed Frank. It was an inevitable step in the career of the rugged redhead, a dedicated football man ever since he was an All-Southwest Conference end at the University of Arkansas in 1939–40.

In 1941 Hickey was drafted by the Pittsburgh Steelers, then coached by the late Bert Bell. He played but one exhibition game before being traded to the Cleveland (now Los Angeles) Rams. Then he spent three years in the Navy, most of it as an officer in charge of gun crews on merchant vessels.

Red returned to the Rams in time to help them win the championship in 1945 and moved out to Los Angeles with the club in 1946. He became an assistant coach to Clark Shaughnessy in 1949 and subsequently served under Joe Stydahar and Hampton Pool. All the Ram assistants resigned en masse after the 1954 season, and Red was almost immediately hired by the 49ers.

Hickey's coaching philosophy, summed up for the sports writers, was simple and direct: "I've been called a 'tough' coach. If that means expecting a hundred per cent effort a hundred per cent of the time from professional football players, then I gladly accept the label."

For his staff, Red retained Mark Duncan and Bill Johnson, and added Bob Shaw, who had been with Baltimore, and Jack Christiansen, who had completed a brilliant playing career with Detroit.

Almost to a man, the football prophets had dire forecasts

A new generation of 49er stars. *Above:* Abe Woodson and Dave Baker. *Below:* Eddie Dove and Tommy Davis

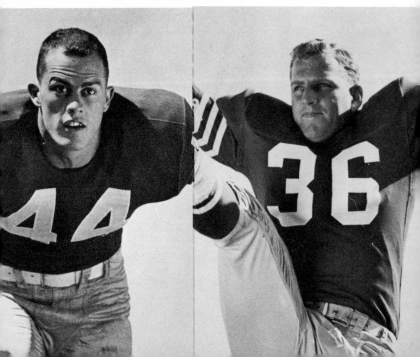

for the 49ers of 1959. A few local writers, with their fingers crossed, said a fourth-place finish was possible. The consensus, however, was for a basement berth in the Western Conference. But John Steadman, perceptive sports editor of the Baltimore *News-Post,* flatly predicted that the Colts would find the 49ers their toughest opposition for first place.

The 49ers' pre-season record—two wins and four setbacks —was certainly nothing to promote hope for a successful season. However, observers close to the club realized that Hickey and his aides were experimenting with numerous position switches, as well as giving vital game experience to the rookies.

The fine crop of newcomers was due in large measure to an intensified talent scouting program under the direction of Lynn (Pappy) Waldorf. The rotund Waldorf joined the 49ers in January of 1957 after more than thirty years of coaching in the college ranks, principally at Northwestern and California. His acceptance of the 49er offer was not only a ten-strike for the San Francisco club but also pro football in general. Still a member of the board of trustees of the American College Football Coaches Association, he is admired and respected on every campus in the country.

By the time the season started, five rookies had captured starting jobs: defensive halfbacks Eddie Dove of Colorado and Dave Baker of Oklahoma; defensive end Charlie Krueger of Texas A&M; linebacker Clancy Osborne of Arizona State (Tempe) ; and offensive tackle Monte Clark of Southern California. In addition, Tommy Davis of Louisiana State became the club's punting and place-kicking specialist.

Before the first league game with Philadelphia, Hickey was discussing the team's chances with several newspapermen. When they reminded him that the 49ers had been picked almost unanimously for last place, Red told them, "I'd sooner pick this team for first than last!"

Above: Jim Pace finds a big hole in Pittsburgh line and races 11 yards for score. *Below:* McElhenny hustles 19 yards with pass from Brodie

(Photos courtesy Frank Rippon)

His optimism seemed justified, at least temporarily: the 49ers dispatched the Eagles, 24–14. Punt runbacks of 65 yards by Abe Woodson and 62 yards by Dove led to two touchdowns.

But the fearsome Rams were next. They had slaughtered the 49ers, 48–14, in the exhibition meeting only three weeks previously and were heavy favorites to do it again at San Francisco.

Hickey had other plans and began setting the trap when the writers gathered in the locker room after the Eagle game. As expected, someone asked, "Do you think you have a chance against Los Angeles?"

"We not only have a chance—we'll beat them!" replied Hickey.

"Do you really mean that?"

"I'll say it fifty times if you want me to—we're going to beat the Rams. And I don't care if they paste this statement up in their dressing room."

The Rams chuckled—and got out the paste pot. They couldn't be blamed for not taking Hickey seriously. The 49ers had become their favorite patsies.

The outcome was unbelievable—a 34–0 win for the 49ers. J. D. Smith and Perry scored on runs of 20 and 32 yards; Billy Wilson took a 13-yard touchdown pass from Tittle; and Tommy Davis kicked a field goal to make it 24–0 at the half.

Smith tallied again and Davis added a 32-yard place kick for all the scoring in the second half. The Rams didn't get past the 49ers' 38-yard line.

As the game ended, the telephone in a press box booth rang. It was answered by one of the city firemen assigned to the park.

"This is Commissioner Bell calling," a voice said. "How did the game come out?"

"Thirty-four to nothing," the fireman replied.

"Well, I guess it was to be expected. Those Rams are rugged."

"No, not the Rams, the 49ers," said the fireman. "The 49ers won."

"Young man," huffed Bell, "I told you this is the commissioner. Don't try to kid me."

Bert was finally convinced that he had heard the correct score.

The 49er dream was interrupted at Green Bay. The Packers, also a surprise team in 1959, came from behind in the fourth period to win, 21–20. The last 49er chance fizzled in the final minute when Davis, hampered by a tricky cross wind, missed a field goal attempt from the Green Bay 37. The sad news of Bert Bell's sudden death put a final period to the disastrous Sunday.

But spirit told. The players chipped in to buy a birthday present for the heartbroken Davis. The gift brought Tommy —and the team—out of the doldrums. On Sunday at Detroit, sharp blocking by the offensive line, particularly guards Bruce Bosley and Ted Connolly, shook Smith loose for 152 yards and Perry for 145. The Lions were muzzled, 34–13.

Smith and Perry were the men of the hour, but the defensive players also came in for their share of the credit. The young secondary of Baker and Dove at safeties and Mertens and Woodson at wings was hailed as potentially the best in 49er history. Mertens, a twenty-first-draft choice, had been a big surprise as a rookie in 1958. Woodson, former Big 10 sprint champion, had played in only four or five games the previous season after being discharged from the Army.

Then the Bears came to San Francisco. The teams traded punishment and points; the 49ers forged ahead, 13–10, with three minutes remaining.

Baker was shaken up on a tackle and had to leave the game. The Bears immediately completed three straight passes for 83

Above: J. D. Smith picks up first down against Baltimore on pass from Tittle. *Below:* Ed Henke's rush against Johnny Unitas falls short

(Wide World Photo)

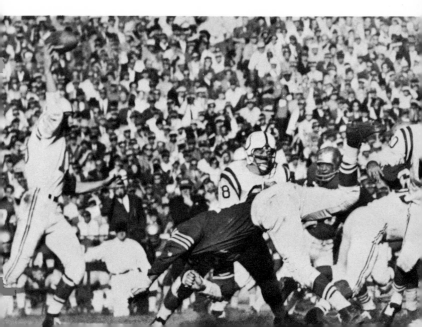

yards and a touchdown. Then the 49ers launched their last-minute fireworks.

Passes from Tittle to Lenny Lyles and Billy Wilson carried San Francisco to the Chicago 45. With sixty-one seconds left, Tittle fought off Bear rushers, ducking under one foe, and ran to his right. Owens dashed downfield, but the Bears, fully expecting the Alley Oop, hounded him with a two-man escort. To work, the pass and reception had to be perfectly executed, and both were. Tittle's high bob was exactly on target—the right-hand corner of the end zone. Almost nonchalantly Owens leaped, and the 49ers had won another cliffhanger, 20–17.

Detroit was humbled again, 33–7, as J. D. Smith set the pattern on the second play of the game with a 73-yard touchdown runoff tackle. With half the schedule gone, the 49ers, at 5–1, had a one-game bulge on the field. Twice before, in 1952 and 1957, they had led by the same margin and faded in the stretch. Would this team collapse? Could it beat the jinx and win its first league game in Los Angeles since 1953?

"This team won't panic," Hickey snapped when interviewers put the questions. "These players have a lot of poise and confidence in themselves."

Despite the brightness of the hour, Red was whistling in the dark—and knew it. The club had been hit by a rash of minor but bothersome injuries, especially to offensive linemen. Worst of all, Tittle, the standby of the 49er attack for six years, was simply not himself.

Only two or three people besides Hickey knew that Y. A. had had at least two dizzy spells during the season. Tittle blamed them on a severe attack of influenza during training camp, combined with his asthma. Drs. O'Grady and O'Connor, however, were worried about the possibility of Ménière's disease, a rare disturbance of the middle ear which causes loss of balance.

Opposing scouts, studying Tittle in action and looking at his record for the first six games, must have realized there was something wrong. The Bald Eagle of the 49ers, who had compiled the best completion record of any active NFL quarterback—better than 55 per cent—had connected on only 46 per cent of his passes. Some of his throws were ludicrously far from the intended targets.

The doctors put Y. A. through extensive tests and could find no definite trace of the Ménière's ailment. So it was on to Los Angeles and the rematch with the revenge-hungry Rams.

Tittle eased the tension by having a good afternoon—8 completions in 14 attempts for 137 yards, including a touchdown pass to Billy Wilson that covered 57 yards. The 49ers didn't sew up their 24–16 victory until Woodson tucked away a Ram kickoff 5 yards deep in the end zone and went all the way. He got vicious blocking from the 49er wedge that included Bob St. Clair, Matt Hazeltine, John Gonzaga, Bill Herchman, Henry (Hawk) Schmidt, and Bruce Bosley. His co-safety, Lenny Lyles, also contributed a key block. The Rams' bid for a fourth-period comeback was broken by Nomellini, who blocked a crucial conversion attempt.

The same afternoon, Baltimore was upset by Washington and the 49ers now had a two-game margin with five to go. The coming road trip was ominous—Bears, Colts, and Browns—but hearts in San Francisco were light and gay.

Wrigley Field, November 15, marked the beginning of the end, although the 49ers were to stay in the race until the next to last game. The Bears took the kickoff and scored without relinquishing the ball. Tittle completed his first pass for 8 yards. Then McElhenny broke into the clear—and Y. A.'s throw wasn't within 10 yards of him. On the next play, Tittle was again far off the mark, and the ball was intercepted.

When the 49ers started their second offensive series, Brodie

R. C. Owens (27) plucks last-minute Tittle pass from hands of defenders on Green Bay goal line

(Wide World Photo)

was in at quarterback. Tittle stayed on the bench until there were only five minutes to play. He seemed to have regained his composure, completing four passes to take the 49ers to the Bear 31. Then, harried by a strong Chicago rush, he watched in horror as another aerial sailed directly into the clutches of Bill George, the middle linebacker.

The benching of Tittle, even more than the 14–3 loss, aroused a storm of controversy in San Francisco. Y. A. was philosophical about the incident, saying: "I was having a bad day and Red benched me. That's all there is to it."

The rumors, both vicious and funny, ranged from hints that Hickey made a "deal" with Chicago gamblers to a story that Tittle was so drunk in the dressing room before the game he couldn't stand up.

Red was caught in the middle. If he began alibiing this late in his career, everyone would smell a mouse. If he told the story of Tittle's balance trouble, it could shake the confidence of the entire squad. And besides, Y. A. determinedly denied that he had suffered any more "spells." Hickey said nothing.

The 49ers lined up at Baltimore with a one-game lead over the Colts. Two hours and fifteen minutes later the Western Conference race was all tied up and San Francisco had been handed one of its worst beatings—48–14. The 49er offense, which had collapsed at Chicago, stayed dormant at Baltimore and was joined in futility by the defense.

All sorts of negative team records were established: fewest total yards, 133; fewest yards rushing, 35; fewest total plays, 33; fewest total first downs, 3. The unkind fates saved their cruelest blow for the fourth quarter when Tittle, who had practically no protection throughout the game, was hammered to the turf by three Colts—in all, 750 pounds of impoliteness.

Even the lionhearted Y. A. couldn't withstand such pressure and he was carried off to the hospital with a knee injury.

J. D. Smith on the loose

(Wide World Photo)

The doctors agreed that his return before the end of the schedule was dubious.

The 49ers had come out of the depths at New York in 1957; now they repeated the story at Cleveland. John Brodie threw two touchdown passes in the second period and McElhenny scored on a 12-yard burst around end. The 21 points held up for a one-point victory as a battling defense, inspired by Charlie Krueger, kept the Browns from getting close enough for a field goal attempt by the immortal Lou Groza.

Jubilantly, the 49ers bade farewell to the road and returned to football-happy San Francisco for the showdown with Baltimore. The team had always been fierce at home. In the friendly confines of Kezar, the 49ers had never lost a finale and had triumphed six times in the next-to-last game.

The Colts didn't bother to brush up on 49er history. In high gear after their early-season shakiness, they displayed their class with a convincing 34–14 win. The incomparable

Johnny Unitas hit his receivers with an ease that was practically disdainful. The speedy Colt secondary stole six San Francisco passes, another all-time negative mark for the 49ers. Not even a brief appearance by Tittle, who had baffled the doctors again by his fast recovery, could lift the 49ers to the heights they had scaled at Cleveland.

A tie was still possible if the Rams upset the Colts the next Saturday, and if the 49ers could down the greatly improved Packers on Sunday. San Franciscans found themselves in the strange position of rooting for their old enemies while watching the nationally televised game from the Coliseum. The Rams gave it the good try before bowing to a fourth-quarter Baltimore explosion.

Green Bay had some hideous plans of its own. Trailing by 14 points after one period, the Packers deadlocked the game by half time and waxed stronger as the afternoon wore on. For the first time in the 49ers' fourteen-year history, including the All-America Conference, the scoreboard posted victory for the final visiting club, 36–14.

As Tittle, who had played the entire game, trudged wearily off the field, a young fan ran up to him and gave vent to that age-old cry of the disappointed rooter: "You guys are a bunch of bums!"

The battle-scarred quarterback smiled wryly and replied: "Maybe you're right, son. But I'll tell you this—we never quit trying."

Tittle's poignant words touched the essence of 49er spirit—a spirit that may have wavered at times, yet never lost the inspiration instilled by Tony Morabito. Hundreds of thousands of football partisans throughout the nation, as well as in the San Francisco Bay Area, respected the 49ers as a fighting outfit, a spectacular and colorful team. The record-breaking crowds they attracted in city after city were the memorial that Tony would have appreciated most.

Emerson (Bud) Spencer, sports editor of the San Francisco *News,* summed it all up in the column he wrote the day after Tony died:

That strong-minded, kindly meaning body of a fine man may be stilled forever out yonder, but his memory, the ring of his voice, his ever ready quiet smile and the things he fought for and lived for, and the things he stood for, they will live on and on. Such things don't die.

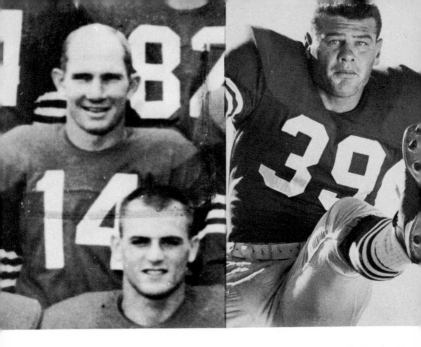

All-time 49ers. *Above:* Yelberton Abraham Tittle and Hugh Mc-Elhenny. *Below:* Joe Perry and Billy Wilson

CHAPTER 15

Stars, Staff, and Press

YELBERTON ABRAHAM TITTLE

No one, teammates or foes, begrudged Yelberton Abraham Tittle the honor when a Congressional subcommittee disclosed that, through 1956, he was the highest-paid player in professional football. His salary then was listed as $21,000 and can safely be said to have jumped steadily during the past three seasons.

"He is all guts—the best battler in the league," says Les Richter of the Los Angeles Rams.

He has more nicknames than any other 49er player—"Y.A.," "Yat," "Colonel Slick" and "Bald Eagle," to state a few. Jane Eshleman Conant, who interviewed him last year for the San Francisco *News-Call Bulletin,* wrote:

The nicknames involving his baldness should be scrapped at once. Tittle, off the field, is bald, of course, but a personable and even handsome man, articulate, soft-spoken and with a spicy touch of humor.

His gray-blue eyes are deep-set under sandy eyebrows. His hair is sandy-blond, his fair skin burned by training camp sun, and his hands are big, square, well-manicured—and capable, as any 49er fan knows.

Tittle was born in Marshall, Texas, October 24, 1926. Yelberton is an old family name and the Abraham was dropped in because his parents believed a Biblical appellation was necessary. His father, now deceased, was a postoffice employee and encouraged both Y. A. and his older brother Jack to participate in all sports, especially football.

Jack starred at Tulane and was drafted by the Philadelphia Eagles but did not go into pro ball. A younger brother, Don, played at Kilgore Junior College.

"Kids in that part of Texas would rather play football than eat," says Tittle. "There were organized leagues even in grammar school, and my first thrill came at eleven when my team was in the district play-offs. In junior high, my hero was Sammy Baugh, then at Texas Christian. I still wish I could throw as well as him."

Tittle was an all-state halfback at Marshall High in 1943 and college scouts, especially representatives of Texas schools, were interested in his future plans. Their ardor was tempered somewhat by the knowledge that he had suffered asthma attacks since childhood.

Y. A. chose Louisiana State. Under the relaxed wartime rules, he was eligible for the varsity as a seventeen-year-old freshman.

"I didn't set the football world on fire," he recalls. "We were using the single wing, and I was lucky to be the fourth-string tailback."

When he was a sophomore, however, L.S.U. shifted to the T formation, and Tittle found his home in football. For three consecutive years he was named the team's most valuable player and was selected for the All-Southeastern Conference team in 1946–47.

He had his most embarrassing moment in his senior season when he intercepted a pass against Mississippi and headed for the distant goal line. Just as a touchdown seemed certain, his pants dropped around his knees and he fell, in tangled humiliation, on the Ole Miss 10-yard line.

Drafted by the Cleveland Browns, then in the All-America Conference, he was traded to Baltimore before the season began. Before reporting to the Colts in July of 1948, he married his high school sweetheart, Minnette De Loach.

He was the rookie of the year and led the Colts to a tie for the Eastern Division title in the AAC. But the next season was disastrous, and in 1950 Tittle found himself playing second fiddle to a newcomer, Adrian Burk. He regained the top job from Burk by midseason.

Picked by the 49ers when the players from the defunct Colts were placed in the draft pool, he spent most of 1951 watching Frankie Albert run the show. Halfway through 1952 the positions were reversed. Y. A.'s supremacy was challenged by Earl Morrall in 1956 and then John Brodie took the controls at the beginning of the 1958 season. Again Tittle battled tooth-and-nail for his job, and again he won.

In 1960, Tittle could surpass Baugh's principal all-time pro records—if his two years in the AAC were counted. In sixteen seasons, the immortal Sammy attempted 3,016 passes and completed 1,709 for 22,085 yards. In twelve years, Tittle has fired 2,960 passes and connected on 1,627 for 21,937 yards.

Y. A.'s move to San Francisco was important in another way: he went into the insurance business, and his Palo Alto brokerage is now one of the most successful in the Bay Area. The $75,000 home he recently built in Atherton, one of San Francisco's most exclusive suburbs, for Minnette and Dianne, ten, Mike, eight, and Pat, six, is proof of that.

HUGH McELHENNY

They call him "The King." Since 1952 he has been the "thrill runner" par excellence, "poetry in motion," murder in a broken field. In 1947 he ran the high hurdles in fourteen seconds flat (an interscholastic record that stood for years), and his six-foot-one, 198-pound frame packs a deceptive power that has bowled over the best tacklers in the NFL.

Hugh claims he runs fast because he's "scared"—not only by 49er opponents but also by the memory of a boyhood incident. When he was six years old he talked his way into a pickup game on a vacant lot in his home city of Los Angeles. The owner of the property arrived with a shotgun—and fired it. Several pellets lodged in the McElhenny backside.

"When I carry the ball," Hugh says, "I think of that man and his shotgun."

Speed alone doesn't make a great runner. McElhenny rises above the ordinary with his ability to cut in or out, to swerve out of a tackler's grasp with churning knee action and the use of an almost forgotten weapon—the straight arm.

He credits Bill Sloan, his coach at Washington High in Los Angeles, with showing him the fine points of packing a football.

"Bill taught me to run with my head as well as my feet. He showed me how a straight arm could be a runner's best protection against a single tackler."

Upwards of forty colleges and universities, from the Atlantic to the Pacific, offered McElhenny athletic scholarships. After one year at Compton Junior College Hugh enrolled at the University of Washington in the fall of 1949.

His press clippings had preceded him, and his reception was cool. Few, however, could know him for even a short time and not be won over by his modest and unassuming personality. Unfortunately, there was an anti-McElhenny faction that spread the stories he was "hard to handle" and was receiving fabulous sums in return for his football services. Most college football stars of the past thirty years have endured similar gossip.

His professional career speaks for itself. All of his coaches—Shaw, Strader, Albert, and Hickey—have said that as a 49er, on and off the field, he has been a pleasure to work with. His non-football pursuits bear out his serious approach to the problem of getting ahead.

After his spectacular rookie year in 1952, Hugh had his choice of numerous jobs. Bypassing more lucrative offers, he accepted a job with a growing Oakland, California, potato chip firm. "The King" drove a delivery truck, sold potato chips, and learned promotion and merchandising. In five years he was head of his own department. Armed with this experience—and the savings he had accumulated—he recently purchased a half interest in one of San Francisco's fastest-growing construction companies.

Working with Hugh every step of the way has been his wife, the former Peggy Ogston of Los Angeles, whom he met in junior high school. They live in a new home in the Los Altos hills with their two daughters, Karen, seven, and Susan, four.

LEO NOMELLINI

Although Horatio Alger did not dwell on athletic themes, he would have appreciated the story of Leo (The Lion) Nomellini. Leo was born in Lucca, Italy, near the Leaning Tower of Pisa. He was a few months under two years of age when his parents emigrated to Chicago and settled in a tenement on the Northwest Side. He had no opportunity to participate in sports during his grammar and high school days. Every nickel was a serious matter in the Nomellini household,

All-time 49ers. Bob St. Clair and Leo Nomellini, with Dr. James
O'Connor, associate team physician, retired Navy Captain

and Leo helped the family budget by selling newspapers and working in a foundry.

The day after he received his high school diploma he enlisted in the Marine Corps and was sent to Cherry Point, North Carolina. Because of his size, he was told that his off-duty hours could be well spent with the football squad. As slight as it was, this background came in handy three years later when, after combat service in the Pacific, including Okinawa, he received his discharge and sought the advantages of higher education.

Bernie Bierman, long-time coach at Minnesota, had been a colonel in the Marine Corps. For him, Nomellini's football inexperience was counterbalanced by his service as a leatherneck and his rugged six-foot-three, 250-pound physique.

Enrolling at the Minneapolis institution, Leo was a starting lineman in the first college football game he had ever seen. As a junior and senior, he was almost unanimously chosen an All-America tackle. In addition, he was Big 10 heavyweight wrestling champion and ran on the Gophers' mile relay team.

San Francisco, with its large population of Italian descent, was a "natural" for Nomellini, not only for football with the 49ers but also for wrestling. Under the astute management of promoter Joe Malcewicz, Leo, soon nicknamed "The Lion," became the greatest mat draw in Bay Area history. His two "world championship" matches with Lou Thesz drew so much attention that sports columnists, who had ignored professional wrestling for years, gave the attraction almost feverish attention.

The second match, held at the spacious Cow Palace, drew an all-time San Francisco record gate of $57,000. Wrestling addicts still contend that Leo won the "championship" that evening; he broke even with Thesz on falls and had his hand upraised when the title holder resorted to foul tactics. But the California Athletic Commission solemnly ruled that the title could not be won on a foul.

During his Minnesota undergraduate days, Leo met Ruth Carole Benson, daughter of a Minneapolis restaurant owner and sportsman. Ruth Carole gave up a modeling career to marry the strong boy from Chicago, and now they live in Palo Alto, California, with their two daughters and a boxer dog named Bronko.

FLETCHER JOE PERRY

The optimists who say a man is as old as he feels have a powerful argument in Fletcher Joe (The Jet) Perry, who in 1960 will be in his thirteenth year as a 49er star.

Offensive fullbacks, who absorb as much punishment as any football player, just aren't supposed to last that long. The fullback in the pro T formation must have the speed to skirt the ends and plunging power to hit the "brier patch" inside the tackles, where he is met by the full fury of the defensive linemen and the linebackers as well.

Perry has fulfilled the assignment so well he is now the leading ground-gainer in football history. His ten seasons in the NFL show the staggering total of 7,151 yards in 1,415 carries —a 5-yard average. Counting his two years in the AAC, the total is 1,607 attempts for 8,496 yards and a 5.2 average.

His feats become even more startling when you remember his contemporaries—Steve Van Buren, Philadelphia; Marion Motley, Cleveland; Fran Rogel, Pittsburgh; Howie Ferguson, Green Bay; "Deacon Dan" Towler and "Tank" Younger, Los Angeles.

Now there is a new generation of linebusters, led by Jim Brown of Cleveland, Alan Ameche of Baltimore, and Rick Casares of the Chicago Bears. Barring injuries, they are the only ones with an opportunity to surpass Perry's marks—and The Jet will make it more difficult with every appearance.

Joe was born in Stevens, Arkansas, and grew up in Los Angeles. His first football experiences were in violation of his mother's order not to participate in the rough sport. One day he was brought home with a broken ankle. She told him: "Joe, if you still want to play football after something like this, go ahead and play—but don't lie to me!"

She was the proudest person present when, in September of 1955, 49er fans honored Joe with a "day"—completely furnishing his new home.

Commentators often use the old saw about great Negro athletes being "a credit to their race as well as to the sport." Perry, the first Negro player signed by the 49ers, is more than that. He's a San Francisco institution, an example for youths of all colors. Perhaps Hugh McElhenny summed it up best when he said: "Joe confers a distinction by letting you line up with him."

The so-called "color line" was broken years ago in pro football, but it still crops up in the heat of competition. A few seasons ago, Perry became the target. The Jet, concerned as usual with only doing his best, finally could stand it no longer. "Quit wasting your wind, bud," he said. "I heard that kind of stuff when you were still in diapers!"

During the off season, The Jet owns and manages one of San Francisco's largest downtown service stations. He plans to expand the business into an area-wide chain when his playing days are over.

BILLY GENE WILSON

The 49ers have three favorite nicknames for Billy Wilson— "Goose," "P. W.," and "Poor Devil."

The first two refer to his build—he's six feet four, 185

pounds, long-necked, and generally resembles a famished prisoner of war. The third concerns his job: he must charge 10 to 15 yards into the secondary, turn his back to hurtling tacklers, and risk life and limb to catch the hook passes that are the bread and butter of a pro passing offense.

A shock of straight black hair and prominent cheekbones go into Billy's physical make-up, attesting to the Sac and Fox Indian blood that courses through his veins. Born on a reservation near Sayre, Oklahoma, he grew up in Campbell, California, forty miles south of San Francisco.

Typically, he took a special speed-up course so he could graduate six months early from Campbell High and enlist in the Navy in 1943. He served as a signalman on patrol craft in the western Pacific.

At San Jose State, he was the school's foremost football and basketball player. In his senior year he entered a wrestling tournament as a lark and won the heavyweight title, pinning his opponent in twenty-nine seconds.

Buddy Parker, then coach of the Detroit Lions, put the stamp of approval on Billy in his rookie year of 1951: "He will become one of the top receivers in the league and the toughest to cover."

The words were prophetic, for it was Wilson who took a 34-yard touchdown pass to help knock the Lions out of the championship that same year.

He tied for the receiving leadership in 1955 with 53 and was in the No. 1 spot alone in 1956 with 60 and again in 1957 with 52. His nine-year total of 404 receptions (for 5,851 yards and 48 touchdowns) is second only to Don Hutson in NFL history.

"Billy's value to the 49ers isn't restricted to his pass receiving," says Coach Red Hickey. "He is a wonderful team man, an inspiration to the other players. He works harder in practice than the greenest rookie. After a game you can ask him how many passes he caught and he can't tell you. He's concerned only with the team effort."

Several years ago Billy purchased a half interest in a San Jose sporting goods store. He also has developed resort property at Lake Tahoe. He and his wife live in Campbell with two sons and a daughter.

BOB ST. CLAIR

San Francisco fans who were present at the 49ers' first intra-squad scrimmage in July of 1953 will never forget it. Bob St. Clair, six-foot-nine, 265-pound rookie tackle from Tulsa, met head-on with Leo Nomellini.

An anthropologist from Stanford later likened it to the struggle of two dinosaurs. Neither player gave ground, on offense or defense, and the 49ers realized they had discovered a new star.

St. Clair, the tallest man in pro football, is the only native San Franciscan on the club. In his junior high school days, he fell in with a gang that barely stayed on the right side of the law.

"We were headed for disaster," he says, "and some of those boys did wind up in prison. I was lucky, for I found that playing football gave me a lot more thrills and satisfaction than 'borrowing' a car and going for a wild ride."

Bob enrolled at the University of San Francisco and was an All-Coast end on the unbeaten-untied-uninvited team of 1951 that sent nine players into pro ball, including Gino Marchetti, Ollie Matson, Joe Scudero, Roy Barni, Red Stephens, and Dick Stanfel. When the school dropped football, Bob transferred to Tulsa for one year before joining the 49ers in 1953.

A born leader, "The Geek" was co-captain of the 49ers in 1957–58, sharing the honor with Nomellini. For the past two years he has been a city councilman in Daly City, a San Francisco suburb, and has serious aspirations for a political career.

Bob's biggest personal thrill came in an exhibition game with the New York Giants at Seattle in 1955. The big guy had had three teeth extracted the afternoon before the game and wasn't counted on for playing duty.

But he went all the way on offense and was on the field when a 49er pass was intercepted by Emlen Tunnell, the Giants' swift halfback. Tunnell had a clear field ahead and a touchdown appeared inevitable. The huge St. Clair, covering ground like a maddened bull elephant, stunned 49,000 people by catching the New Yorker from behind.

A polished and effective speaker, Bob is in demand on the banquet circuit. He has taken a sincere interest in juvenile problems and frequently visits detention homes and reform schools, where his own story has a far-reaching impact on boys who have been in trouble.

He is a sales manager for a San Francisco air freight concern and lives in Daly City with his wife, Ann, and four children.

GORDON LEROY SOLTAU

Even though he is no longer active as a player, a book about the 49ers wouldn't be complete without more personal mention of Gordy Soltau.

During his nine-year career, he was the game saver, the clutch guy who made fantastic catches or came through with accurate place kicks as the final seconds ticked off. No other 49er player was ever more popular or made a deeper impression on the football public in the San Francisco area. When he retired after the 1958 season, Gordy was the third leading scorer in NFL history with 644 points.

At the age of three, in his home town of Duluth, Minnesota,

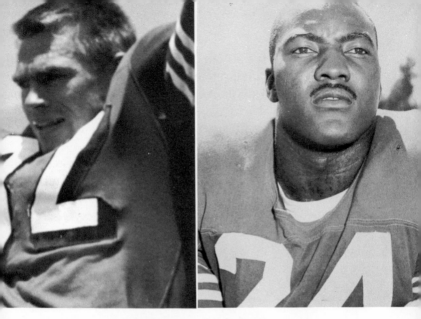

Gordy Soltau and J. D. Smith

he lost the sight in his left eye. Vision was restored several years later but Gordy always wore glasses off the field.

At the University of Minnesota he won varsity letters in football, basketball, and ice hockey. He was an outstanding pitcher in sandlot baseball. Enlisting in the Navy in 1942, he became one of the original "Frogmen" and was later detached to the cloak-and-dagger Office of Strategic Services for operations that included swimming up to five miles. Several years ago he won the California Class B slalom championship and undoubtedly could have qualified as one of the nation's top skiers if he had been able to devote more time to the sport.

In 1950, his first year in pro ball, Gordy was used primarily as a defensive end. He got his chance to play offense in 1951, and he and Billy Wilson had few, if any, peers as a combination at the wings.

In 1952 he was a member of the Northern California Eisenhower for President Speakers' Bureau.

Not content with a prosaic off-season job with a leading San Francisco office supply firm, he formed a 49er basketball team which has annually played twenty-five to thirty games in communities around San Francisco. In 1958, the 49er cagers and the Harlem Globetrotters attracted a crowd of 14,000 to the San Francisco Cow Palace.

Last year, Gordy became one of the 49er radio-television commentators and, as usual, the job he turned in won critical acclaim from all sources.

Gordy married his college sweetheart, Nancy Olson, and they live in Palo Alto, California, with their two sons and daughter.

J. D. SMITH

Johnny Unitas of the Baltimore Colts is the "Cinderella Man" of the National Football League, but J. D. Smith of the 49ers runs him a close second.

J. D.—he swears he has no given names—came out of little North Carolina A&T in 1956 to join the Chicago Bears. He was dropped after six games, and the 49ers, desperately in need of defensive halfbacks, signed him.

Actually, Red Hickey, then an assistant coach, had an idea that J. D. would be more effective on offense with his 207 pounds and 9.7 timing in the 100-yard dash. But the needs of the moment took precedence, and J. D. was a defender through the 1957 season.

He had times of acute frustration and despair, especially in the closing games of 1957 when 49er audiences booed lustily every time his name was announced on the public address system. The mistakes of a defensive back, especially when he permits a receiver to get behind him, are all too apparent to the people in the stands.

"Just go out there and do your best," Hickey told him.

"The guys that are booing you now will be cheering for you next year."

In 1958, with Perry and McElhenny having excellent seasons at the tight back positions, J. D. spent most of the time on the bench. But he got those cheers predicted by Hickey when he ran 80 yards for a touchdown against Green Bay.

Destiny took over at the beginning of 1959. Perry was set at fullback, but McElhenny was moved to the flanker, and Jim Pace, expected to be the No. 1 tailback, was injured. Smith found security as a halfback and became one of the few men in NFL history to gain more than 1,000 yards in a single season—1,036, to be exact. He carried the ball 207 times, an all-time 49er record but still 83 less than the league leader, Jim Brown of Cleveland. J. D. averaged 5 yards per carry against 4.6 for Brown. His teammates voted him the Len Eshmont Memorial Award—a $1,000 watch.

In the off season, J. D. is a playground supervisor for the Norfolk, Virginia, recreation department. He is married and has two children.

OTHER 49er VETERANS

Football coaches speak in reverent tones of players who are "willing to pay the price." Such a performer is Ed Henke, veteran defensive end whose effort against the Chicago Bears in 1957 will be long remembered. . . . Handsome Ted Connolly and Bruce Bosley are rated among the best offensive guard combinations in the NFL. Connolly realized his boyhood dream when he was drafted by the 49ers, for he grew up in Oakland, across the bay. Bosley was named on the St. Louis *Sporting News'* All-NFL team in 1959. . . . The same honor was accorded Matt Hazeltine, one of the most improved linebackers in the league. Matt was six feet, 197 pounds when he

Red Hickey's coaching staff for 1960. *Above:* Frank Albert and Jack Christiansen. *Below:* Mark Duncan and Bill Johnson

reported in 1955; now he's six feet one, 220, and retains his agility and speed afoot. . . .

Clyde Conner was recognized mostly for his basketball prowess at College of Pacific, playing barely enough football to win one letter. Scout Joe Vetrano saw him in a spring practice game and signed him as a free agent. Clyde has ranked among the league's leading receivers for four seasons. . . .

Bill Herchman will never forget the biggest thrill of all for a lineman—intercepting a pass and running 54 yards for a touchdown against the Chicago Bears. . . . Jim Ridlon has been the handy man in the defensive backfield, filling in at any position. . . . The 9.5 speed of backs Lenny Lyles and Jim Pace makes them two of the most dangerous runners in the league. . . .

John Brodie, a professional golfer from January to July, has been in the shadow of Y. A. Tittle at quarterback, yet John has had his moments of glory, especially against Baltimore as a rookie in 1957 and against Cleveland in 1959. . . .

The 49ers' defensive backfield of Abe Woodson, Jerry Mertens, Dave Baker, and Eddie Dove should become the best in the club's history. Woodson was named on the United Press International's All-Pro team in 1959. Both he and Baker were picked for the Pro Bowl. Mertens was a twentieth-draft choice from Drake University. . . .

Tommy Davis, a kicking specialist, is aiming at Gordy Soltau's scoring records. . . . Monte Clark is among the many Southern California alumni who have made good with the 49ers. . . . C. R. Roberts, another ex-Trojan, was signed as a fullback for the final game of 1959 and contributed a long touchdown run. . . .

Johnny Thomas failed with the club as an offensive end in 1957, then returned the following year to win a job as a tackle, a rarity in pro ranks. . . . Lanky Karl Rubke has the potential to become an outstanding linebacker, and Frank Morze, if he can overcome a weight problem, could be a fixture at center for years. . . . A chronic knee ailment has handicapped the career of linebacker Clancy Osborne, a dedicated football player. . . .

If any single defensive lineman were picked for future greatness, it would have to be Charlie Krueger, the big Texan. . . . Henry (Hawk) Schmidt and John Wittenborn have specialized in the "suicide squads"—the kickoff teams. . . . Center-linebacker Bob Harrison had his rookie year almost wasted because of a summer accident that required more than eighty stitches in his leg. . . .

OWNERS AND FRONT OFFICE

The San Francisco 49ers are a limited partnership, with controlling interest held by Mrs. Josephine Morabito, widow of Tony, and Victor P. Morabito.

The club is Victor's principal business interest and he spends full time in his front-office capacity as president.

Most recent additions to the list of owners are Louis G. Spadia, who is also 49er general manager, and Frank C. Albert. Other co-owners are:

Dr. William E. O'Grady, prominent San Francisco physician and surgeon.

Albert J. Ruffo, San Jose attorney and member of the board of governors of the California Bar Association.

Lawrence J. Purcell, San Francisco insurance broker.

James A. Ginella, retired construction engineer.

Franklin Mieuli, owner of Station KPUP in San Francisco and producer of radio and television sports programs.

Permanent front-office employees include Nathan Scardigli, comptroller; Peter Giannini, ticket director; Mrs. Wanda Murray, assistant ticket director; Roy Gilbert, assistant to

Lynn Waldorf; Patricia Lorenz, secretary; and Mrs. Evelyn Hoffman, secretary-PBX.

Robert J. (Buzz) McGee, a former Santa Clara football star, was the 49ers' publicity director during the four years of the All-America Conference and made a vital contribution to the establishment of pro football in San Francisco.

From 1953 to 1959, Bill Kim, now a Honolulu attorney, divided his time between law school and the 49ers, working as assistant publicity director and chief aide in the talent scouting department.

Legal problems are in the capable hands of Marshall Leahy, who has also acted for the National Football League in many crucial cases.

The colorful 49er band, wearing authentic miner garb of the Gold Rush days, is directed by Joseph McTigue, who also is in charge of all half-time entertainment.

TEAM ASSISTANTS

Henry (Schmidty) Schmidt, nationally famous trainer for the University of Santa Clara for more than thirty years, joined the 49ers in 1956 as successor to Robert (Pop) Kleckner. The latter, generally recognized as the greatest all-around athlete in University of San Francisco athletic history, was with the 49ers as head trainer from 1946 until he resigned to open his own physical therapy business. Before coming to the 49ers, the peppery Schmidty helped out at the Los Angeles Rams' training camps for a number of years.

At training camp and during the season, Schmidty is assisted by Lincoln Kimura, chief trainer at San Jose State College.

The unsung but important job of equipment manager was held first by Zigmund (Ziggy) Zamlynsky, who came to the

49ers as a halfback aspirant from Villanova. A foot injury ended his football career but Ziggy stayed with the club as equipment man until enticed away by an offer from the Pillsbury Company in Philadelphia. He was replaced by Franklin Clark, now Pacific sales director for the Burgermeister Brewing Company.

Raymond (Chico) Norton has held the job since 1955 and spends the off season on the grounds staff of the San Francisco Giants.

RADIO AND TELEVISION

A veteran crew of sports announcers handles the telecasts and radio broadcasts of all 49er games:

Bob Fouts, who does the play-by-play on either radio or television, has been associated with the club since its formation. His chief co-workers are Gordy Soltau, a 49er immortal, and Lon Simmons, who also announces the San Francisco Giants' baseball games. The veteran Russ Hodges gives a hand on occasion, as does Bob Blum.

The late NFL Commissioner Bert Bell with sports reporters Jack McDonald, *Call-Bulletin*; Bruce Lee, *Chronicle*; Prescott Sullivan, *Examiner*; Bill Leiser, *Chronicle*; Dink Templeton, KFRC; Bob Brachman, *Examiner*

Currently covering the 49ers in the press, radio and television are the following:

San Francisco *News-Call Bulletin*—Roger Williams, Jack McDonald, Walt Daley.

San Francisco *Chronicle*—Art Rosenbaum, Bill Leiser, Darrell Wilson.

San Francisco *Examiner*—Bob Brachman.

Oakland *Tribune*—Alan Ward, Wally Willis, Ray Haywood.

Station KSFO, San Francisco—Lon Simmons, Bill King, Bob Blum.

Station KGOX, San Francisco—Ira Blue.

Station KNBC, San Francisco—Hal Wolf.

Station KCBS, San Francisco—Don Klein.

Station KFAX, San Francisco—Dave Schofield.

Redwood City *Tribune*—Ed Jacoubowsky, Dink Templeton.

San Mateo *Times*—Jack Bluth, Jack Russell.

Burlingame *Advance-Star*—Bill Warden.

San Jose *Mercury-News*—Jack Hanley, Louis Duino, Bill Feist.

Richmond *Independent*—Ed Levitt.

Vallejo *Times-Herald*—Dave Beronio.

Berkeley *Gazette*—Jim Scott, Bob Law.

Hayward *Review*—Sid Hoos.

San Leandro *Morning News*—Win Currier.

Alameda *Times-Star*—Jack Clark.

Stockton *Record*—John Peri.

Sacramento *Bee*—Wilbur Adams.

Sacramento *Union*—Bob McCarthy.

Chico *Enterprise-Record*—Eddie Booth.

Salinas *Californian*—Ernie Olson.

Monterey *Peninsula-Herald*—Bob Bullock.

United Press International—Hal Wood, Scott Baillie.

Associated Press—Jack Stevenson, Al Cline.

Station KSRO, Santa Rosa—Dan Galvin.

Fresno *Bee*—Ed Orman.

Woodland *Democrat*—Don Bloom.

Pittsburgh *Post-Dispatch*—Charlie Zeno.

Antioch *Ledger*—Ken McDonald.

San Rafael *Independent-Journal*—Jim Gilmartin, John Connolly.

Lodi *News-Sentinel*—Carl Underwood.

Los Gatos *Times*—John Baggerly.

Marysville *Appeal-Democrat*—Lee Sota.

Modesto *Bee*—Jim Roach.

Petaluma *Argus-Courier*—Jay Ross.

Contra Costa *Gazette*—Jerry Gandy.

49er Team Statisticians—S. Dan Brodie, Richard L. Conner, William R. Hall, C. George Ross.

Record Section

ALL-TIME 49ER ROSTER
1946-59

Player	Position	School	Years Played
ALBERT, Frank	QB	Stanford	1946-52
ALDRIDGE, Ben	HB	Oklahoma A&M	1952
ARENAS, Joe	HB	Omaha	1951-57
ATKINS, Bill	HB	Auburn	1958-59
BABB, Gene	FB	Austin	1957-58
BABCOCK, Harry	E	Georgia	1953-55
BAHNSEN, Ken	HB	North Texas State	1953
BAKER, Dave	HB	Oklahoma	1959
BALATTI, Ed	E	Oakland (Cal.) High	1946-48
BALDWIN, John	C	Centenary	1947
BANDUCCI, Bruno	G	Stanford	1946-54
BARNES, Larry	HB	Colorado	1957
BASSI, Dick	G	Santa Clara	1946-47
BEALS, Alyn	E	Santa Clara	1946-51
BEATTY, Ed	C	Mississippi	1955-56
BENTZ, Roman	T	Tulane	1948
BERRY, Rex	HB	Brigham Young	1951-56
BOONE, J. R.	HB	Tulsa	1952
BOSLEY, Bruce	G	West Virginia	1956-59
BRODIE, John	QB	Stanford	1957-59
BROWN, Hardy	LB	Tulsa	1951-55
BROWN, Pete	C	Georgia Tech	1953-54
BRUCE, Gail	E	Washington	1948-51
BRUMFIELD, Jackson	E	Mississippi Southern	1954
BRUNEY, Fred	HB	Ohio State	1953, 1956
BRYANT, Bob	T	Texas Tech	1946-49
BURKE, Don	LB	Southern California	1950-54
CAMPBELL, Marion	T	Georgia	1954-55
CAMPORA, Don	T	College of Pacific	1950, 1952
CARAPELLA, Al	T	Miami (Fla.)	1951-55
CARPENTER, John	T	Michigan	1949
CARR, Eddie	HB	Olney High (Pa.)	1947-49
CARR, Paul	LB	Houston	1955-58
CASANEGA, Ken	HB	Santa Clara	1946, 1948
CASON, Jim	HB	Louisiana State	1948-52, 1954
CASSARA, Frank	FB	St. Mary's	1954
CATHCART, Royal	HB	Santa Barbara State	1950
CATHCART, Sam	HB	Santa Barbara State	1949-50, 1952
CAVELLI, Tony	C	Stanford	1949
CLARK, Don	G	Southern California	1948-49
CLARK, Monte	T	Southern California	1959
COLLIER, Floyd	T	San Jose State	1948
COLLINS, Ray	T	Louisiana State	1950-52
CONLEE, Gerry	C	St. Mary's	1946-47
CONNER, Clyde	E	College of Pacific	1956-59

Player	Position	School	Years Played
CONNOLLY, Ted	G	Santa Clara-Tulsa	1954, 1956-59
COX, James	G	Stanford	1948
CROSS, Bob	T	Kilgore, J.C.	1956-57
CROWE, Paul	HB	St. Mary's	1948
CROWELL, Otis	T	Hardin-Simmons	1947
DAHMS, Tom	T	San Diego State	1957
DAVIS, Tommy	K	Louisiana State	1959
DOVE, Eddie	HB	Colorado	1959
DOW, Harley	G	San Jose State	1950
DUGAN, Fred	E	Dayton	1958-59
DUNCAN, Maury	QB	San Francisco State	1954-55
DURDAN, Don	HB	Oregon State	1946-47
ELLIOTT, Charles	T	Oregon	1948
ELSTON, Art	C	South Carolina	1946-48
ENDRISS, Al	E	San Francisco State	1952
ESHMONT, Len	HB	Fordham	1946-49
EVANS, Ray	G	Texas Western	1949-50
EVANSEN, Paul	G	Oregon State	1948
FEHER, Nick	G	Georgia	1951-54
FISK, Bill	E	Southern California	1946-47
FORREST, Ed	C	Santa Clara	1946-47
FRANCESCHI, Pete	HB	San Francisco	1946
FREITAS, Jesse	QB	Santa Clara	1946-47
GALIFFA, Arnie	QB	West Point	1954
GARLIN, Don	HB	Southern California	1949-50
GEHRKE, Fred	HB	Utah	1950
GOAD, Paul	FB	Abilene Christian	1956
GONZAGA, John	T	Mt. Diablo (Cal.) High	1946-52
GRGICH, Visco	G	Santa Clara	1946-52
HALL, Forrest	HB	San Francisco	1948
HALL, Parker	HB	Mississippi	1946
HANLEY, Dick	C	Fresno State	1947
HANTLA, Bob	G	Kansas	1954-55
HARDY, Carroll	HB	Colorado	1955
HARKEY, Lem	HB	Emporia State	1955
HARRISON, Bob	LB	Oklahoma	1959
HAZELTINE, Matt	LB	California	1955-59
HENKE, Ed	E	Southern California	1951-52, 1955-59
HERCHMAN, Bill	T	Texas Tech	1956-59
HOBBS, Homer	G	Georgia	1950-51
HOGLAND, Doug	G	Oregon State	1953-55
HOLLADAY, Bob	HB	Tulsa	1956-57
HORNE, Dick	E	Oregon	1947
HOWELL, Clarence	E	Texas A&M	1948

Player	Position	School	Years Played
JESSUP, Bill	E	Southern California	1951-52, 1954-59
JOHNSON, John Henry	HB	St. Mary's-Ariz. State	1954-56
JOHNSON, Bill	C	Tyler J.C.	1948-56
KENNY, Charles	G	San Francisco	1947
KRAEMER, Eldred	G	Pittsburgh	1955
KRUEGER, Charles	E	Texas A&M	1959
KUZMAN, John	T	Fordham	1946
LAND, Fred	T	Louisiana State	1948
LAUGHLIN, Bud	FB	Kansas	1955
LEDYARD, Hal	QB	Chattanooga	1953
LILLYWHITE, Verl	HB	Southern California	1948-51
LIVINGSTON, Howie	HB	Fullerton J.C.	1950
LOYD, Alex	E	Oklahoma A&M	1950
LUNA, Bob	HB	Alabama	1955
LYLES, Leonard	HB	Louisville	1959
McCORMICK, Tom	HB	College of Pacific	1956
McELHENNY, Hugh	HB	Washington	1952-59
MALONEY, Norm	E	Purdue	1948-49
MANLEY, Joe	LB	Mississippi State	1953
MASINI, Leonard	FB	Fresno State	1947-48
MATHESON, Riley	LB	Texas Western	1948
MATHEWS, Ned	HB	U.C.L.A.	1946-47
MATTHEWS, Clay	E	Georgia Tech	1950, 1953-55
MATUSZAK, Marv	LB	Tulsa	1957-58
McCORMICK, Walt	C	Southern California	1948
MELLUS, John	T	Villanova	1946
MERTENS, Jerry	HB	Drake	1958-59
MEYERS, Bob	FB	Stanford	1952
MICHALIK, Art	G	St. Ambrose	1953-54
MIKE, Bob	T	U.C.L.A.	1948-49
MILLER, Hal	T	Georgia Tech	1953
MIXON, Bill	HB	Georgia	1953-54
MOEGLE, Dick	HB	Rice	1955-59
MOMSEN, Bob	G	Ohio State	1952
MONACHINO, Jim	HB	California	1951
MORGAN, Joe	T	Mississippi Southern	1949
MORRALL, Earl	QB	Michigan State	1956
MORRIS, Dennit	LB	Oklahoma	1958
MORRIS, George	C	Georgia Tech	1956
MORTON, John	LB	Texas Christian	1953
MORZE, Frank	C	Boston College	1957-59
NIX, Jack	E	Southern California	1950
NOMELLINI, Leo	T	Minnesota	1950-59
NORBERG, Hank	E	Stanford	1946-47

Player	Position	School	Years Played
O'DONAHUE, Pat	E	Wisconsin	1952
OSBORNE, Clancy	LB	Arizona State (Temple)	1959
OWENS, R. C.	HB	College of Idaho	1957-59
PACE, Jim	HB	Michigan	1958
PALATELLA, Lou	G	Pittsburgh	1955-58
PARSONS, Earle	HB	Southern California	1946-47
PAVLICH, Chuck	G	Muskegon (Mich.) High	1946
PERRY, Joe	FB	Compton J.C.	1948-59
POWELL, Charles	E	San Diego (Cal.) High	1952-53, 1955-57
POWERS, Jim	QB	Southern California	1950-53
PUDDY, Harold	T	Oregon	1948
QUILTER, Chuck	T	Tyler, J.C.	1949
REMINGTON, Bill	C	Washington State	1946
RENFRO, Dick	FB	Washington State	1946
RIDLON, Jim	HB	Syracuse	1957-59
ROBNETT, Ed	HB	Texas Tech	1947
ROSKIE, Ken	FB	South Carolina	1946
RUBKE, Karl	C	Southern California	1957-59
RUCKA, Leo	C	Rice	1956
SABUCO, Tino	C	San Francisco	1949
SAGELY, Floyd	E	Arkansas	1954-56
SALATA, Paul	E	Southern California	1949-50
SANDIFER, Dan	HB	Louisiana State	1950
SARDISCO, Tony	G	Tulane	1956
SATTERFIELD, Alf	T	Vanderbilt	1947
SCHABARUM, Pete	HB	California	1951, 1953-54
SCHIECHL, John	C	Santa Clara	1947
SHARKEY, Ed	G	Nevada	1955-56
SHAW, Charles	G	Oklahoma A&M	1950
SHERIFF, Stan	LB	California Poly	1956-57
SHOENER, Hal	E	Iowa	1948-50
SITKO, Emil	HB	Notre Dame	1950
SMITH, Charles	E	Abilene Christian	1956
SMITH, Ernie	HB	Compton J.C.	1955-56
SMITH, George	C	California	1947
SMITH, J. D.	HB	North Carolina A&T	1956-59
SMITH, Jerry	G	Wisconsin	1952-53
SOLTAU, Gordy	E	Minnesota	1950-58
SPARKS, Dave	G	South Carolina	1951
SPENCE, Julian	HB	Sam Houston	1957
STANDLEE, Norm	FB	Stanford	1946-52

Player	Position	School	Years Played
STITS, Bill	HB	U.C.L.A.	1957-58
STOLHANDSKE, Tom	LB	Texas	1955
STRICKLAND, Bishop	FB	South Carolina	1951
STRZYKALSKI, John	HB	Marquette	1946-52
ST. CLAIR, Bob	T	San Francisco-Tulsa	1953-59
SULLIVAN, Bob	HB	Holy Cross	1948
SUSOEFF, Nick	E	Washington State	1946-49
TANNER, Hamp	T	Georgia	1951
TERESA, Tony	HB	San Jose State	1958
THOMAS, John	T	College of Pacific	1958-59
THORNTON, Rupe	G	Santa Clara	1946-47
TIDWELL, Billy	HB	Texas A&M	1954
TITCHENAL, Bob	E	San Jose State	1946
TITTLE, Y. A.	QB	Louisiana State	1951-59
TONEFF, Bob	T	Notre Dame	1952, 1954-58
TUBBS, Jerry	LB	Oklahoma	1958-59
VAN DOREN, Bob	E	Southern California	1953
VAUGHT, Ted	E	Texas Christian	1955
VETRANO, Joe	HB	Mississippi Southern	1946-49
WAGNER, Lowell	HB	Southern California	1949-53
WALLACE, Bev	QB	Compton J.C.	1947-49
WALKER, Val Joe	HB	Southern Methodist	1957
WHITE, Bob	HB	Stanford	1951-52
WILLIAMS, Joel	C	Texas	1948
WILLIAMS, John	HB	Southern California	1954
WILSON, Billy	E	San Jose State	1951-59
WISMANN, Pete	LB	St. Louis	1949-52, 1954
WITTENBORN, John	G	Southeast Missouri	1958-59
WOODSON, Abe	HB	Illinois	1958-59
WOUDENBERG, John	T	Denver	1946-49
YONAMINE, Wally	HB	Farrington (Honolulu) High	1947
YOUNGELMAN, Sid	T	Alabama	1955
YOWARSKY, Walt	C	Kentucky	1958
ZAMLYNSKY, Zigmond	HB	Villanova	1946

ALL-TIME SCORES — 1946-1959

ALL-AMERICA CONFERENCE
(1946-1949)

1946

COACH: LAWRENCE T. SHAW

49ers		Opp.
7	New York Yankees	21
21	Miami Seahawks	14
32	Brooklyn Dodgers	13
7	Chicago Rockets	21
34	Miami Seahawks	7
22	Los Angeles Dons	14
14	Buffalo Bills	17
34	Cleveland Browns	20
27	Buffalo Bills	14
7	Cleveland Browns	14
9	New York Yankees	10
30	Brooklyn Dodgers	14
14	Chicago Rockets	0
48	Los Angeles Dons	7

W - 9   L - 5

1947

COACH: LAWRENCE T. SHAW

49ers		Opp.
23	Brooklyn Dodgers	7
17	Los Angeles Dons	14
14	Baltimore Colts	7
16	New York Yankees	21
41	Buffalo Bills	24
28	Baltimore Colts	28
42	Chicago Rockets	28
7	Cleveland Browns	14
26	Los Angeles Dons	16
16	New York Yankees	24
14	Cleveland Browns	37
41	Chicago Rockets	16
21	Brooklyn Dodgers	7
21	Buffalo Bills	21

W - 8   L - 4   T - 2

1948

COACH: LAWRENCE T. SHAW

49ers		Opp.
35	Buffalo Bills	14
36	Brooklyn Dodgers	20
41	New York Yankees	0
36	Los Angeles Dons	14
38	Buffalo Bills	28
31	Chicago Rockets	14
56	Baltimore Colts	14
21	New York Yankees	7
21	Baltimore Colts	10
44	Chicago Rockets	21
7	Cleveland Browns	14
63	Brooklyn Dodgers	40
28	Cleveland Browns	31
38	Los Angeles Dons	21

W - 12   L - 2

1949

COACH: LAWRENCE T. SHAW

49ers		Opp.
31	Baltimore Colts	17
42	Chicago Hornets	7
42	Los Angeles Dons	14
17	Buffalo Bills	28
42	Chicago Hornets	24
56	Cleveland Browns	28
51	Buffalo Bills	7
3	New York Yankees	24
28	Cleveland Browns	30
28	Baltimore Colts	10
41	Los Angeles Dons	24
35	New York Yankees	14

W - 9   L - 3

* 17	New York Yankees	7
# 7	Cleveland Browns	21

* Play-off Game.
# Championship Game.

ALL-TIME SCORES — 1946 - 1959 (Cont'd)

NATIONAL FOOTBALL LEAGUE

1950

COACH: LAWRENCE T. SHAW

49ers		Opp.
17	New York Yanks	21
20	Chicago Bears	32
14	Los Angeles Rams	35
7	Detroit Lions	24
24	New York Yanks	29
28	Detroit Lions	27
17	Baltimore Colts	14
21	Los Angeles Rams	28
14	Cleveland Browns	31
0	Chicago Bears	17
21	Green Bay Packers	25
30	Green Bay Packers	14

W-3   L-9

1951

COACH: LAWRENCE T. SHAW

49ers		Opp.
24	Cleveland Browns	10
14	Philadelphia Eagles	21
28	Pittsburgh Steelers	24
7	Chicago Bears	13
44	Los Angeles Rams	17
16	Los Angeles Rams	23
19	New York Yanks	14
21	Chicago Cardinals	27
10	New York Yanks	10
20	Detroit Lions	10
31	Green Bay Packers	19
21	Detroit Lions	17

W-7   L-6   T-1

1952

COACH: LAWRENCE T. SHAW

49ers		Opp.
17	Detroit Lions	3
37	Dallas Texans	14
28	Detroit Lions	0
40	Chicago Bears	16
48	Dallas Texans	21
17	Chicago Bears	20
14	New York Giants	23
23	Washington Redskins	17
9	Los Angeles Rams	35
21	Los Angeles Rams	34
7	Pittsburgh Steelers	24
24	Green Bay Packers	14

W-7   L-5

1953

COACH: LAWRENCE T. SHAW

49ers		Opp.
31	Philadelphia Eagles	21
31	Los Angeles Rams	30
21	Detroit Lions	24
35	Chicago Bears	28
10	Detroit Lions	14
24	Chicago Bears	14
31	Los Angeles Rams	27
21	Cleveland Browns	23
37	Green Bay Packers	7
38	Baltimore Colts	21
48	Green Bay Packers	14
45	Baltimore Colts	14

W-9   L-3

ALL-TIME SCORES - 1946 - 1959 (Cont'd)

NATIONAL FOOTBALL LEAGUE (Cont'd)

1954

COACH: LAWRENCE T. SHAW

49ers		Opp.
41	Washington Redskins	7
24	Los Angeles Rams	24
23	Green Bay Packers	17
31	Chicago Bears	24
37	Detroit Lions	31
27	Chicago Bears	31
34	Los Angeles Rams	42
7	Detroit Lions	48
31	Pittsburgh Steelers	3
13	Baltimore Colts	17
35	Green Bay Packers	0
10	Baltimore Colts	7

W - 7   L - 4   T - 1

1955

COACH: NORMAN P. STRADER

49ers		Opp.
14	Los Angeles Rams	23
3	Cleveland Browns	38
20	Chicago Bears	19
27	Detroit Lions	24
23	Chicago Bears	34
38	Detroit Lions	31
14	Los Angeles Rams	27
0	Washington Redskins	7
21	Green Bay Packers	27
14	Baltimore Colts	26
7	Green Bay Packers	28
35	Baltimore Colts	24

W - 4   L - 8

1956

COACH: FRANK C. ALBERT

49ers		Opp.
21	New York Giants	38
33	Los Angeles Rams	30
7	Chicago Bears	31
17	Detroit Lions	20
21	Chicago Bears	38
13	Detroit Lions	17
6	Los Angeles Rams	30
17	Green Bay Packers	16
10	Philadelphia Eagles	10
20	Baltimore Colts	17
38	Green Bay Packers	20
30	Baltimore Colts	17

W - 5   L - 6   T - 1

1957

COACH: FRANK C. ALBERT

49ers		Opp.
10	Chicago Cardinals	20
23	Los Angeles Rams	20
21	Chicago Bears	17
24	Green Bay Packers	14
21	Chicago Bears	17
35	Detroit Lions	31
24	Los Angeles Rams	37
10	Detroit Lions	31
21	Baltimore Colts	27
27	New York Giants	17
17	Baltimore Colts	13
27	Green Bay Packers	20

W - 8   L - 4

*27	Detroit Lions	31

* Play-off for Western Conference
Championship.

ALL-TIME SCORES — 1946-1959 (Cont'd)

NATIONAL FOOTBALL LEAGE (Cont'd)

	1958			1959	
	COACH: FRANK C. ALBERT			COACH: HOWARD W. HICKEY	
49ers		Opp.	49ers		Opp.
23	Pittsburgh Steelers	20	24	Philadelphia Eagles	14
3	Los Angeles Rams	33	34	Los Angeles Rams	0
6	Chicago Bears	28	20	Green Bay Packers	21
30	Philadelphia Eagles	24	34	Detroit Lions	13
14	Chicago Bears	27	20	Chicago Bears	17
24	Detroit Lions	21	33	Detroit Lions	7
7	Los Angeles Rams	56	24	Los Angeles Rams	16
21	Detroit Lions	35	3	Chicago Bears	14
33	Green Bay Packers	12	14	Baltimore Colts	48
27	Baltimore Colts	35	21	Cleveland Browns	20
48	Green Bay Packers	21	14	Baltimore Colts	34
21	Baltimore Colts	12	14	Green Bay Packers	36

| W-6   L-6 | W-7   L-5 |

SAN FRANCISCO 49ers NAMED ON ALL-PRO TEAMS — 1946-59
(SELECTIONS OF UNITED PRESS INTERNATIONAL OR ASSOCIATED PRESS)

1947 — *Offense:* Bruno Banducci, guard.

1951 — *Offense:* Leo Nomellini, tackle.

1952 — *Offense:* Gordy Soltau, end; Leo Nomellini, tackle; *Hugh McElhenny, halfback.

1953 — *Offense:* Bruno Banducci, guard; Hugh McElhenny, halfback; Joe Perry, fullback.
   Defense: Leo Nomellini, tackle.

1954 — *Offense:* Bruno Banducci, guard; Joe Perry, fullback.
   Defense: Leo Nomellini, tackle.

1955 — *Offense:* Billy Wilson, end; Bob St. Clair, tackle.
   Defense: Bob Toneff, tackle.

1957 — *Offense:* **Y. A. Tittle, quarterback; Billy Wilson, end.
   Defense: Leo Nomellini, tackle; Marv Matuszak, linebacker.

1959 — *Offense:* J. D. Smith, halfback.
   Defense: Leo Nomellini, tackle; Abe Woodson, halfback.

* McElhenny named United Press "Rookie of the Year" and *Sport* magazine's "Player of the Year."

** Tittle named United Press International's "Player of the Year."

SAN FRANCISCO 49ers SELECTED FOR PRO BOWL GAME—1951-60:

1951 — Leo Nomellini, Visco Grgich, Frank Albert, John Strzykalski,
Norm Standlee.

1952 — Leo Nomellini, Ray Collins, Jim Cason, Gordy Soltau.

1953 — Bill Johnson, Ed Henke, Gordy Soltau, Leo Nomellini,
Hugh McElhenny, Joe Perry.

1954 — Gordy Soltau, Bill Johnson, Leo Nomellini, Joe Perry,
Art Michalik, Y. A. Tittle, Hugh McElhenny.

1955 — Bruno Banducci, *Billy Wilson, Y. A. Tittle, John Henry
Johnson, Joe Perry, Al Carapella, Jim Cason.

1956 — Billy Wilson, Bob Toneff, Dick Moegle.

1957 — Bob St. Clair, Hugh McElhenny, Billy Wilson, Leo Nomellini.

1958 — Billy Wilson, *Hugh McElhenny, Y. A. Tittle, Leo Nomellini,
Marv Matuszak.

1959 — Bob St. Clair, Billy Wilson, Leo Nomellini, Hugh McElhenny,
Jerry Mertens.

1960 — Billy Wilson, Leo Nomellini, Dave Baker, Abe Woodson,
Bob St. Clair, J. D. Smith.

* Named Most Valuable Player.

49er ALL-TIME STANDINGS

All-America Conference

	W.	L.	T.	Pct.	Pts.	Op. Pts.	Div. Stdg.
1946	9	5	0	.643	307	189	2nd
1947	8	4	2	.667	327	264	2nd
1948	12	2	0	.857	495	248	2nd
1949	9	3	0	.750	416	227	*
Totals	38	14	2	.731	1445	924	---

* AAC had round-robin schedule. San Francisco lost championship play-
off to Cleveland, 21 - 7.

National Football League

	W.	L.	T.	Pct.	Pts.	Op. Pts.	Div. Stdg.
1950	3	9	0	.250	213	300	Tied 5th
1951	7	4	1	.636	255	205	Tied 2nd
1952	7	5	0	.583	285	221	3rd
1953	9	3	0	.750	372	237	2nd
1954	7	4	1	.636	313	251	3rd
1955	4	8	0	.333	216	298	5th
1956	5	6	1	.455	233	284	3rd
1957	8	4	0	.667	260	264	**Tied 1st
1958	6	6	0	.500	257	324	4th
1959	7	5	0	.583	255	237	Tied 3rd
Totals	63	54	3	.547	2659	2421	---

** 49ers lost divisional play-off to Detroit, 31 - 27.

49er ALL-TIME CAREER LEADERS

Passing

	Atts.	Comp.	Yds.	TDs	Pct. Comp.	Int.
FRANK C. ALBERT						
1946-49 (AAC)	963	515	6948	88	53.5	55
1950-52	601	316	3847	27	52.6	43
	1564	831	10795	115	53.1	98
YELBERTON A. TITTLE						
1948-49 (Balt. AAC)	578	309	4731	30	53.5	27
1950 (Balt. NFL)	315	161	1884	8	51.1	19
1951-59	2067	1157	15322	104	56.0	131
	2960	1627	21937	142	55.0	177

Receiving

	No.	Yds.	TDs
BILLY G. WILSON			
1951-59	*404	5851	48

* Second only to Don Hutson in NFL history.

	No.	Yds.	TDs
GORDON L. SOLTAU			
1950-58	249	3363	25
ALYN BEALS			
1946-49 (AAC)	177	2510	46
1950-51	34	441	3
	211	2951	49
HUGH McELHENNY			
1952-59	165	2359	14
JOE PERRY			
1948-49 (AAC)	19	225	4
1950-59	178	1271	7
	197	1496	11
CLYDE CONNER			
1956-59	114	1448	11

Punt Returns

	No.	Yds.	Avg.
JAMES CASON			
1948-49 (AAC)	43	660	15.3
1950-54	24	280	11.7
	67	940	14.1
JOE ARENAS			
1951-57	124	774	6.2

49er ALL-TIME CAREER LEADERS (Cont'd)

Rushing

	Atts.	Yds.	Avg.	TDs
JOE PERRY 1948-49 (AAC)	192	1345	7.01	18
1950-59	*1415	*7151	5.05	56
	1607	8496	5.28	74
HUGH McELHENNY 1952-59	782	3941	5.04	36
JOHN STRZYKALSKI 1946-49 (AAC)	429	2454	5.72	14
1950-52	233	961	4.12	5
	662	3415	5.16	19
NORM STANDLEE 1946-49 (AAC)	375	1734	4.62	17
1950-52	30	96	3.20	1
	405	1830	4.52	18

* A NFL record.

Kickoff Returns

	No.	Yds.	Avg.
JOE ARENAS 1951-57	139	3798	27.3

Punting

	No.	Avg.	Blk.	Lg.
FRANK C. ALBERT 1946-49 (AAC)	160	44.0	1	82
1950-52	139	41.9	1	70
	299	43.0	2	----

Interceptions

	No.	Yds. Ret.	TDs
LOWELL WAGNER 1949 (AAC)	6	121	1
1950-53	25	239	0
	31	360	1

Scoring

GORDON SOLTAU
1950-58

*644 total points (25 touchdowns, 70 field goals, 284 extra points)

* 3rd best in NFL history.

SECTION I
Individual Records

BALL CARRYING

Most Times Carried Ball — Career
1607	Joe Perry	1948-59
1415	Joe Perry (NFL only)	1950-59

Most Times Carried Ball — One Season
207	J. D. Smith	1959

Most Times Carried Ball — One Game
27	Joe Perry, Green Bay	12/15/57

Most Yards Gained — Career
8496	Joe Perry	1948-59
7151	Joe Perry (NFL only)	1950-59

Most Yards Gained — One Season
1049	Joe Perry	1954

Most Yards Gained — One Game
174	Joe Perry, Detroit	11/2/58

Highest Average Gain — Career
5.28 (8496 Yards—1607 Carries)	Joe Perry	1948-59
5.05 (7151 Yards—1415 Carries)	Joe Perry (NFL only)	1950-59
5.04 (3941 Yards—782 Carries)	Hugh McElhenny	1952-59

Highest Average Gain — One Game — 10-15 Attempts
13.23 (174 Yards—13 Carries)	Joe Perry, Detroit	11/2/58

Highest Average Gain — One Game — 16-20 Attempts
9.69 (155 Yards—16 Carries)	Joe Perry, Cleveland (AAC)	10/9/49
9.56 (133 Yards—16 Carries)	Joe Perry, At Green Bay (Mil.)	11/20/55

Highest Average Gain — One Game — Over 20 Attempts
7.23 (159 Yards—22 Carries)	Hugh McElhenny, At Green Bay (Mil.)	11/23/58

PASSING

Most Passes Attempted — Career
2067	Y. A. Tittle	1951-59

Most Passes Attempted — One Season
306	Frank Albert	1950

Most Passes Attempted — One Game
50	Frank Albert, Los Angeles	10/1/50

Section I – Individual Records   **Passing**

Most Passes Completed – Career
1157   Y. A. Tittle   1951-59

Most Passes Completed – One Season
176   Y. A. Tittle   1957

Most Passes Completed – One Game
29   Y. A. Tittle, Baltimore   12/13/53

Highest Completion Percentage – Career
56% (1157 Completions–2067 Attempts)
                                  Y. A. Tittle   1951-59

Highest Completion Percentage – One Season
63.1% (176 Completions–279 Attempts)
                                  Y. A. Tittle   1957

Highest Completion Percentage – One Game – 10-20 Attempts
86.7% (13 Completions–15 Attempts) Frank Albert, At
                                    Baltimore (AAC)   10/10/48
83.3% (15 Completions–18 Attempts) Y. A. Tittle,
                                    Green Bay   12/5/54

Highest Completion Percentage – One Game – 21-30 Attempts
75% (21 Completions–28 Attempts)   Y. A. Tittle, Detroit   11/3/57

Highest Completion Percentage – One Game – 31 or More Attempts
75% (24 Completions–32 Attempts)   Y. A. Tittle, At
                                    Baltimore   11/24/57

Most Yards Gained Passing – Career
15322   Y. A. Tittle   1951-57
10795   Frank Albert   1946-52

Most Yards Gained Passing – One Season
2205   Y. A. Tittle   1954

Most Yards Gained Passing – One Game
371   Y. A. Tittle, Baltimore   12/13/53

Most Passes Had Intercepted – Career
131   Y. A. Tittle   1951-59
95   Frank Albert   1946-52

Most Passes Had Intercepted – One Season
28   Y. A. Tittle   1955

Most Passes Had Intercepted — One Game
5   Y. A. Tittle, At
                                 Baltimore   1/30/58
                               Y. A. Tittle, Baltimore   12/13/53
                               Frank Albert, Pittsburgh 12/7/52

Most Touchdown Passes — Career
115   Frank Albert   1946-52·
104   Y. A. Tittle   1951-59

Most Touchdown Passes — One Season
29   Frank Albert (AAC)   1948
20   Y. A. Tittle   1953

Most Touchdown Passes — One Game
5   Frank Albert,
                                 Cleveland (AAC)   10/9/49
4   Y. A. Tittle, Baltimore   12/13/53

Most Yards Lost Attempting to Pass — One Season
362   Y. A. Tittle   1957

Most Yards Lost Attempting to Pass — One Game
72   Y. A. Tittle,
                                 At Los Angeles   11/10/57

RECEIVING

Most Receptions — Career
404   Billy Wilson   1951-59

Most Receptions — One Season
60   Billy Wilson   1956
                               Billy Wilson   1954

Most Receptions — One Game
11   Billy Wilson,
                                 At Los Angeles   10/3/54

Most Touchdown Passes — Career
49   Alyn Beals   1946-52
48   Billy Wilson   1951-59

Most Touchdown Passes — One Season
14   Alyn Beals (AAC)   1948
10   Billy Wilson   1953

Most Touchdown Passes — One Game
3   Gordy Soltau,
                                  Los Angeles   10/28/51
                               Alyn Beals, At
                                  Chicago (AAC)   9/30/49
                               Alyn Beals, At
                                  Brooklyn (AAC)   11/21/48

Most Yards Receptions — Career
5851   Billy Wilson   1951-59

Most Yards Receptions — One Season
889   Billy Wilson   1956

Most Yards Receptions — One Game
196   Gordy Soltau,
                                  At New York   11/9/52

Highest Average Gain Per Reception — One Season — 10-20 Receptions
28.2 (12 Receptions—388 Yards)   Carroll Hardy   1955

*Highest Average Gain Per Reception — One Season — 21 or More
  Receptions*
18.8 (30 Receptions—565 Yards)   Bill Jessup   **1954**

PASS INTERCEPTIONS

Most Interceptions — Career
31   Lowell Wagner   1949-53
25   Lowell Wagner
                                  (NFL only)   1950-53
25   Jim Cason   1948-52

Most Interceptions — One Season
9   Lowell Wagner   1951
                               Jim Cason (AAC)   1949

Most Interceptions — One Game
3   Dick Moegle,
                                  Chicago Bears   10/27/57
                               Lowell Wagner, Detroit 12/16/51
                               Jim Cason, At
                                  Los Angeles (AAC)   11/13/49
                               Bill Stits, Pittsburgh   9/28/58

Most Yards Interceptions Returned — Career
452   Lowell Wagner   1949-53
404   Rex Berry (NFL only)   1951-56

Most Yards Interceptions Returned – One Season
147   Jim Cason   1951

Most Yards Interceptions Returned – One Game
77 (2 Interceptions)   Ned Mathews,
                                 Buffalo (AAC)   12/7/47
69 (3 Interceptions)   Dick Moegle,
                                 Chicago Bears   10/27/57

KICKOFF RETURNS

Most Kickoffs Returned – Career
139   Joe Arenas   1951-57

Most Kickoffs Returned – One Season
27   Joe Arenas   1956

Most Kickoffs Returned – One Game
5   Joe Arenas, New York   9/30/56
                                 Dick Moegle, At Detroit   10/16/55
                                 Joe Arenas, Cleveland   10/2/55

Most Yards Kickoffs Returned – Career
3798   Joe Arenas   1951-57

Most Yards Kickoffs Returned – One Season
801   Joe Arenas   1956

Most Yards Kickoffs Returned – One Game
158 (3 Returns)   Abe Woodson,
                                 At Los Angeles   11/8/59

Highest Average Kickoff Return – Career
27.3 (139 Returns–3798 Yards)   Joe Arenas   1951-57

Highest Average Kickoff Return – One Season
34.4 (16 Returns–551 Yards)   Joe Arenas   1953

Highest Average Kickoff Return – One Game – 3 or More Returns
52.7 (3 Returns–158 Yards)   Abe Woodson,   11/8/59
                                 At Los Angeles

PUNT RETURNS

Most Punts Returned – Career
124   Joe Arenas   1951-57

Most Punts Returned – One Season
25   Joe Arenas   1957

Most Punts Returned — One Game

8	Hugh McElhenny,	
	Green Bay	11/2/58
	Joe Arenas, At Detroit	10/16/55

Most Yards Punts Returned — Career

774	Joe Arenas	1951-57

Most Yards Returned — One Season

351	Jim Cason (AAC)	1949
284	Hugh McElhenny	1952

Most Yards Punts Returned — One Game

122 (3 Returns)	Hugh McElhenny, At	
	Chicago Bears	10/19/52

Highest Average Punt Return — Career

6.55 (99 Returns—648 Yards)	Hugh McElhenny	1952-59
6.24 (124 Returns—774 Yards)	Joe Arenas	1951-57
14.03 (67 Returns—940 Yards)	Jim Cason	1948-54

Highest Average Punt Return — One Season

16.7 (21 Returns—351 Yards)	Jim Cason (AAC)	1949
15.7 (11 Returns—173 Yards)	Jim Cason	1950

Highest Average Punt Return — One Game — 3 or More Returns

40.7 (3 Returns—122 Yards)	Hugh McElhenny,	
	At Chicago Bears	10/19/52

PUNTING

Most Punts — Career

299	Frank Albert	1946-52
139	Frank Albert (NFL only)	1950-52

Most Punts — One Season

68	Frank Albert	1952

Most Punts — One Game

11	Pete Brown, At	
	Chicago Bears	10/17/54

Most Yards Punting — Career

12864	Frank Albert	1946-52
5828	Frank Albert (NFL only)	1950-52

Most Yards Punting — One Season

2899	Frank Albert	1952

Most Yards Punting — One Game
418   Pete Brown, At
                                        Chicago Bears   10/17/54

Highest Punting Average — Career — 100 or More Punts
43.0 (299 Punts—12864 Yards)   Frank Albert   1946-52
41.9 (139 Punts—5828 Yards)   Frank Albert (NFL only) 1950-52

Highest Punting Average — One Season — 30 or More Punts
48.2 (31 Punts—1495 Yards)   Frank Albert (AAC)   1949
45.7 (59 Punts—2694 Yards)   Tommy Davis   1959

Highest Punting Average — One Game — 3-6 Punts
54.5 (4 Punts—218 Yards)   Larry Barnes,
                                        Chicago Cardinals   9/29/57

Highest Punting Average — One Game — 7 or More Punts
47.5 (8 Punts—380 Yards)   Bill Jessup, At
                                        Los Angeles   11/10/57

SCORING

Most Points Scored — Career
644 (25 Touchdowns 70 Field Goals, 284 Extra Points)
                                        Gordy Soltau   1950-58

Most Points Scored — One Season
114 (6 Touchdowns, 10 Field Goals, 48 Extra Points)
                                        Gordy Soltau   1953

Most Points Scored — One Game
26 (3 Touchdowns, 1 Field Goal, 5 Extra Points)
                                        Gordy Soltau,
                                        Los Angeles   10/28/51

Most Touchdowns Scored — Career
76   Joe Perry   1948-59
53   Joe Perry (NFL only)   1950-59

Most Touchdowns Scored — One Season
14   Alyn Beals (AAC)   1948
13   Joe Perry   1953

Most Touchdowns Scored — One Game

3	Joe Perry, Baltimore	12/13/53
	Joe Perry, At Chicago Bears	10/18/53
	Gordy Soltau, Los Angeles	10/28/51
	Joe Perry, Buffalo (AAC)	10/16/49
	Alyn Beals, At Chicago (AAC)	9/30/49
	Alyn Beals, At Brooklyn (AAC)	11/21/48
	Frank Albert, At Buffalo (AAC)	9/28/47
	Dick Renfro, Miami (AAC)	9/15/46

Most Extra Points Attempted — Career

302	Gordy Soltau	1950-58

Most Extra Points Attempted — One Season

66	Joe Vetrano (AAC)	1948
49	Gordy Soltau	1953

Most Extra Points Attempted — One Game

9	Joe Vetrano, At Brooklyn (AAC)	11/21/48
7	Gordy Soltau, Dallas	10/26/52
	Gordy Soltau, Green Bay	12/7/58

Most Extra Points — Career

284 (302 Attempts)	Gordy Soltau	1950-58

Most Extra Points — One Season

62 (66 Attempts)	Joe Vetrano (AAC)	1948
48 (49 Attempts)	Gordy Soltau	1953

Most Extra Points — One Game

9	Joe Vetrano, At Brooklyn (AAC)	11/21/48
7	Gordy Soltau, Dallas	10/26/52

Most Field Goal Attempts — Career

138	Gordy Soltau	1950-58

Most Field Goal Attempts — One Season

26	Tommy Davis	1959

Section I — Individual Records   Scoring

Most Field Goal Attempts — One Game
6   Gordy Soltau, At
                                     Green Bay (Mil.)   11/23/58

Most Field Goals — Career
70   Gordy Soltau   1950-58

Most Field Goals — One Season
13   Gordy Soltau   1956

Most Field Goals — One Game
4   Gordy Soltau,
                                     Los Angeles   10/7/56

Highest Extra Point Percentage — Career — 100 or More Attempts
94% (302 Attempts—284 Made)   Gordy Soltau   1950-58

Highest Extra Point Percentage — One Season — 30 or More Attempts
100% (56 Attempts—56 Made)   Joe Vetrano (AAC)   1949
     (33 Attempts—33 Made)   Gordy Soltau   1957
     (31 Attempts—31 Made)   Tommy Davis   1959

Highest Field Goal Percentage — Career — 50 or More Attempts
50.7% (132 Attempts—70 Made)   Gordy Soltau   1950-58

Highest Field Goal Percentage — One Season
66.7% (15 Attempts—10 Made)   Gordy Soltau   1953

SECTION II

TEAM RECORDS

Most Rushing Plays — One Season   603 (AAC)   1948
                                       523   1951

Most Rushing Plays — One Game   56, At Green Bay (Mil.) 10/10/54
                                           Detroit   10/25/53
                                           Baltimore   10/29/50
                                           Los Angeles (AAC)   9/19/48

Fewest Rushing Plays — One Season 359   1958

Fewest Rushing Plays — One Game   15, At Chicago Bears   10/12/58

Most Rushing Plays Allowed — One Season 538   1955

Section II — Team Records

Most Rushing Plays Allowed — One Game	62, At Chicago Bears	11/19/50
Fewest Rushing Plays Allowed — One Season 348		1954
Fewest Rushing Plays Allowed — One Game	13, At Brooklyn (AAC) At Green Bay (Mil.)	11/24/46 10/10/54
Most Yards Rushing — One Season	3663 (AAC) 2498	1948 1954
Most Yards Rushing — One Game	390 Baltimore (AAC) 302 Green Bay	10/24/48 12/9/51
Most Yards Rushing Allowed — One Season	2192	1956
Most Yards Rushing Allowed — One Game	324, At Los Angeles	11/9/58
Fewest Yards Rushing — One Season 1622		1957
Fewest Yards Rushing — One Game 35, At Baltimore		11/22/59
Fewest Yards Rushing Allowed — One Season	873 (AAC) 1371	1946 1954

Fewest Yards Rushing Allowed —
  One Game
	1 At Los Angeles
	  (AAC)
	21 Baltimore
		10/12/46
		10/29/50

Highest Rushing Average — One Season	6.07 (AAC) 5.65	1948 1954
Highest Rushing Average — One Game (24 Plays—263 Yards)	10.96 Dallas	10/26/52
Lowest Rushing Average — One Season (592 Plays—2175 Yards) (408 Plays—1713 Yards)	3.67 (AAC) 4.20	1946 1955
Lowest Rushing Average — One Game (21 Plays—37 Yards)	1.76, At New York	11/9/52

PASSING

Most Passes Attempted — One Season 383		1958
Most Passes Attempted — One Game 50 Los Angeles		10/1/50

Section II – Team Records   Passing

Fewest Passes Attempted –
  One Season   252 (AAC)   1946
                                         264   1959

Fewest Passes Attempted –
  One Game   12 At Los Angeles
                                           (AAC)   12/5/48
                                         14 At Baltimore   11/29/53

Most Passes Completed – One Season   213   1958

Most Passes Completed – One Game   29 Baltimore   12/13/53

Fewest Passes Completed – One Season   130 (AAC)   1946
                                         132   1959

Fewest Passes Completed – One Game   4 Los Angeles (AAC) 9/19/49
                                         Chicago (AAC)   11/30/46
                                       5 At Los Angeles   11/4/51

Highest Completion Percentage – One Season
(305 Attempts–191 Completions)   62.6%   1957

Highest Completion Percentage – One Game
(16 Attempts–20 Completions)   80% At Baltimore (AAC) 10/10/48
(28 Attempts–21 Completions)   75% At Detroit   11/3/57

Lowest Completion Percentage – One Season
(287 Attempts–139 Completions)   48.8% (AAC)   1949
(303 Attempts–151 Completions)   49.8   1955

Lowest Completion Percentage – One Game
(14 Attempts–4 Completions)   28.6% Chicago (AAC)   11/30/46
(14 Attempts–4 Completions)   28.6% Los Angeles (AAC) 9/19/49
(16 Attempts–5 Completions)   31.3% At Los Angeles   11/4/51

Most Net Yards Passing – One Season   2483   1958

Most Net Yards Passing – One Game   345 Baltimore   12/13/53

Most Net Yards Passing Allowed – One Season   2649   1954

Most Net Yards Passing Allowed –
  One Game   387 At Chicago Bears   10/17/54

Fewest Net Yards Passing – One Season   1549   1959

Fewest Net Yards Passing – One Game   11 Los Angeles   10/7/56

Fewest Net Yards Passing Allowed —
One Season   1638   1952

Fewest Net Yards Passing Allowed —
One Game   15 At Brooklyn-New
                                        York (AAC)   10/23/59
                                  25 At Detroit   10/12/52

Most Passes Had Intercepted — One Season   29   1958

Most Passes Had Intercepted — One Game   6 Baltimore   12/5/59

Most Passes Intercepted By — One Season   33   1951

Most Passes Intercepted By —
One Game   7 At Los Angeles
                                        (AAC)   12/5/48
                                  6 At Chicago Bears   10/17/54
                                  6 Los Angeles   10/28/51

Fewest Passes Had Intercepted — One Season   12   1954

Fewest Passes Intercepted By — One Season   14   1959

Most Yards Lost Attempting to Pass — One Season   396   1952

Most Yards Lost Attempting to Pass — One Game   95 Dallas   10/26/52

Most Yards Lost Attempting to Pass by Opponents — One Season
                                                      366   1954

Most Yards Lost Attempting to Pass by Opponents — One Game
                                  75 Detroit   11/11/59

Fewest Yards Lost Attempting to Pass — One Season
                                  136   1959

Highest Average Gain Per Pass Attempt — One Season
                                  7.31 (AAC)   1948
                                  6.96   1951

Highest Average Gain Per Pass Attempt — One Game
                                  13.6 At Baltimore (AAC)   10/5/47
                                  13.3 At Baltimore   12/2/56

TOTAL PLAYS AND YARDAGE

Most Total Yards Gained — One Season
(3663 Rushing—2104 Passing)   5767 (AAC)   1958
(2168 Rushing—2230 Passing)   4398   1953

Section II — Team Records   Total Plays and Yardage

Most Total Yards Gained — One Game   597 Baltimore   12/13/53

Most Total Yards Allowed — One Season
(1906 Rushing—2615 Passing)   4521 (AAC)   1948
(1847 Rushing—2401 Passing)   4248   1957

Most Total Yards Allowed — One Game   577 Los Angeles   11/9/58

Fewest Total Yards Gained — One Season
(1713 Rushing—1938 Passing)   3651   1955

Fewest Total Yards Gained — One Game
(35 Rushing—98 Passing)   133 At Baltimore   11/22/59

Fewest Total Yards Allowed — One Season
(873 Rushing—2150 Passing)   3023 (AAC)   1946
(1566 Rushing—1638 Passing)   3204   1952

Fewest Total Yards Allowed — One Game
(40 Rushing—25 Passing)   65 At Detroit   10/12/52

Most Total Plays — One Season
(603 Rushing—288 Passing)   891 (AAC)   1948
(523 Rushing—281 Passing)   804   1951

Most Total Plays — One Game
(41 Rushing—44 Passing)   85 Chicago Bears   11/1/53

Most Total Plays Allowed — One Season
(538 Rushing—311 Passing)   849   1955

Most Total Plays Allowed — One Game
(54 Rushing—30 Passing)   84 At Los Angeles   11/6/55

Fewest Total Plays — One Season
(408 Rushing—303 Passing)   711   1955

Fewest Total Plays — One Game
(16 Rushing—17 Passing)   33 At Baltimore   11/22/59

Highest Average Gain Per Offensive Play — One Season
                                     6.47 (AAC)   1948
                                     6.02   1954

Highest Average Gain Per Offensive Play — One Game
                                     7.86 Chicago Bears   10/28/56

PUNTING

Most Punts — One Season	68	1952
Most Punts — One Game	11 At Chicago Bears	10/17/54
Fewest Punts — One Season	42	1953
Fewest Punts — One Game	0 Baltimore	12/13/53
Most Yards Punting — One Season	2899	1952
Most Yards Punting — One Game	418 At Chicago Bears	10/17/54
Fewest Yards Punting — One Season	1706	1952
Fewest Yards Punting — One Game	0 Baltimore	12/13/53
Highest Punting Average — One Season	45.7	1959
Highest Punting Average — One Game	54.5 Chicago Cardinals	9/29/57
Lowest Punting Average — One Season	37.0	1954
Lowest Punting Average — One Game	23.3 At Green Bay	11/26/50
Most Punts Blocked — One Season	3 (AAC) 1	1947 1950-51-52-53-55
Most Punts Had Blocked — One Season	3	1955

PUNT RETURNS

Most Punts Returned — One Season	51 (AAC) 40	1946 1952-54
Most Punts Returned — One Game	8 At Detroit	10/12/52
Fewest Punts Returned — One Season	33	1950-53
Most Yards Punt Returns — One Season	713 (AAC) 436	1949 1952
Most Yards Punt Returns — One Game	144 Philadelphia	9/27/59
Fewest Yards Punt Returns — One Season	118	1955

Highest Average Punt Return – One Season
                    15.5 (AAC)   1949
                    12.3   1950

Lowest Average Punt Return – One Season   3.0   1955

KICKOFF RETURNS

Most Kickoffs Returned – One Season 51   1955-56

Most Kickoffs Returned – One Game   9 At Detroit   11/14/54

Fewest Kickoffs Returned – One Season   36   1952

Most Kickoff Return Yards – One Season   1257   1956

Most Kickoff Return Yards – One Game   256 At Detroit   11/14/54

Fewest Kickoff Return Yards – One Season   777 (AAC)   1946
                                   798   1952

Highest Average Kickoff Return – One Season   26.1   1957

Lowest Average Kickoff Return – One Season   19.7 (AAC)   1947
                                  20.0   1950

FIRST DOWNS

Most First Downs Rushing – One Season   134   1951

Most First Downs Rushing – One Game   19 Green Bay   12/9/51

Most First Downs Rushing Allowed – One Season   132   1955

Most First Downs Rushing Allowed – One Game
                        18 At Chicago Bears   10/14/56
                        18 At Baltimore   11/22/59

Fewest First Downs Rushing – One Season   92   1957

Fewest First Downs Rushing – One Game   1 At New York   11/9/52
                              1 At Baltimore   11/22/59

Fewest First Downs Rushing Allowed – One Season   56 (AAC)   1946
                                     74   1954

Fewest First Downs Rushing Allowed – One Game
                  1 At Detroit   10/12/52
                  Baltimore (AAC)   9/14/57
                  At Los Angeles (AAC) 10/14/45

Section II – Team Records   **First Downs**

Most First Downs Passing – One Season   126   1958

Most First Downs Passing – One Game   20 New York   9/30/56

Most First Downs Passing Allowed – One Season   126   1958

Most First Downs Passing Allowed – One Game
                              18 At Baltimore   11/24/57
                              Detroit   10/24/54

Fewest First Downs Passing – One Season
                              52 (AAC)   1946
                              76   1959

Fewest First Downs Passing – One Game
                              1 Los Angeles   10/7/56
                              At Los Angeles (AAC) 12/5/48
                              At Cleveland (AAC)   11/14/48
                              At New York (AAC)   11/17/46
                              New York (AAC)   9/8/46

Fewest First Downs Passing Allowed – One Season   76   1952

Fewest First Downs Passing Allowed – One Game
                              0 Brooklyn-New York
                              (AAC)   10/23/49
                              2 Detroit   11/2/58
                              At Green Bay (Mil.)   11/22/53

Most Total First Downs – One Season   252   1954

Most Total First Downs – One Game   31 Baltimore   12/13/53

Most Total First Downs Allowed – One Season   250   1955

Most Total First Downs Allowed – One Game 29 At Baltimore 11/22/59

Fewest Total First Downs – One Season   170 (AAC)   1946
                                         201   1950

Fewest Total First Downs – One Game   6 New York (AAC)   9/8/46
                                       3 At Baltimore   11/22/59

Fewest Total First Downs Allowed – One Season   140 (AAC)   1946
                                                 167   1952

Fewest Total First Downs Allowed – One Game
                              4 At Detroit   10/12/52
                              Buffalo (AAC)   11/2/46

PENALTIES

Most Penalties Against — One Season   93   1950

Most Penalties Against — One Game   14 At Pittsburgh   11/20/54
                                          At Baltimore   11/29/53
                                          At Chicago Bears   10/19/52

Most Penalties Against Opponents — One Season 72 (AAC)   1948
                                          71   1950–53

Most Penalties Against Opponents — One Game
                                 15 At Cleveland   11/15/53

Fewest Penalties Against — One Season   56 (AAC)   1946
                                                57   1957–59

Fewest Penalties Against — One Game   1 Buffalo (AAC)   10/12/46
                              2 At Los Angeles (AAC)   12/7/47
                                 Green Bay   12/4/55
                                 At Los Angeles   11/6/55
                                 Chicago Bears   10/25/59

Fewest Penalties Against Opponents — One Season   43   1956

Fewest Penalties Against Opponents — One Game
                                 0 At Cleveland   11/29/59

Most Yards Penalized — One Season   851   1950

Most Yards Penalized — One Game   148 At Philadelphia 10/19/58

Most Yards Opponents Penalized — One Season   615   1953

Most Yards Opponents Penalized — One Game
                                 140 At Detroit   10/8/50

Fewest Yards Penalized — One Season   440 (AAC)   1946
                                         489   1959

Fewest Yards Penalized — One Game   10 At Los Angeles   11/6/55
                                 New York (AAC)   11/21/47
                                 At Brooklyn (AAC)   11/24/46

Fewest Yards Opponents Penalized — One Season
                                 321   1956

Fewest Yards Opponents Penalized — One Game
                                 0 At Cleveland   11/29/59

SCORING

Most Touchdowns Scored — One Season   69 (AAC)   1948
                                         49   1953

Most Touchdowns Scored — One Game
                        9 At Brooklyn (AAC)   11/21/48
                        7 Dallas   10/26/52
                          Green Bay   12/7/58

Most Touchdowns Allowed — One Season 42   1958

Most Touchdowns Allowed — One Game   8 At Los Angeles   11/9/58

Fewest Touchdowns Scored — One Season   29   1950

Fewest Touchdowns Scored — One Game
                        0 At Brooklyn-New York (AAC)   10/23/49
                          At Chicago Bears   11/19/50
                          Cleveland   10/2/55
                          At Washington   11/13/55
                          At Los Angeles   11/11/56
                          Los Angeles   10/5/58
                          At Chicago Bears   11/15/59

Fewest Touchdowns Allowed — One Season   24   1951

Fewest Touchdowns Allowed — One Game
                        0 Chicago (AAC)   11/30/46
                          New York (AAC)   9/12/48
                          Detroit   9/28/52
                          At Detroit   10/12/52
                          At Pittsburgh   11/20/54
                          Green Bay   12/5/54
                          Los Angeles   10/4/59

Most Points Scored — One Season   495 (AAC)   1948
                                     372   1953

Most Points Scored — One Game
            63 (9 TD, 9 Xpts) At Brooklyn (AAC)   11/21/48
            48 (7 TD, 6 Xpts) Dallas   10/26/52
               (6 TD, 6 Xpts, 2 FG) Green Bay   12/6/53
               (7 TD, 6 Xpts) Green Bay   12/7/58

Most Points Allowed — One Season   324   1958

Most Points Allowed — One Game
            56 (8 TD, 8 Xpts) At Los Angeles   11/9/58

Section II — Team Records   Scoring

Fewest Points Scored — One Season	213	*1950*
Fewest Points Scored — One Game	0 At Washington	11/13/55
	At Chicago Bears	11/19/50
Fewest Points Allowed — One Season	189 (AAC)	1946
	205	1951
Fewest Points Allowed — One Game		
	0 At Chicago (AAC)	11/24/46
	New York (AAC)	9/12/48
	At Detroit	10/12/52
	Green Bay	12/5/54
	Los Angeles	10/4/59

SECTION III

LONGEST PLAYS

LONGEST RUNS FROM SCRIMMAGE

1.	89 (TD)	Hugh McElhenny	At Dallas	10/5/52
2.	86 (TD)	Hugh McElhenny	At Green Bay	11/18/56
3.	82 (TD)	Hugh McElhenny	Dallas	10/26/52
4.	80 (TD)	J. D. Smith	Green Bay	12/7/58
5.	78 (TD)	Joe Perry	Green Bay	12/10/50
6.	78 (TD)	Joe Perry	Dallas	10/26/52
7.	73 (TD)	Joe Perry	Detroit	11/2/58
	73 (TD)	J. D. Smith	Detroit	11/1/59
8.	71	Hugh McElhenny	Detroit (Div. Playoff)	12/22/57
9.	67	Pete Schabarum	Los Angeles	10/28/51
10.	65 (TD)	Earle Parsons	Los Angeles (AAC)	10/12/46
	65 (TD)	Forrest Hall	Chicago (AAC)	11/7/48

LONGEST FORWARD PASS PLAYS

1.	78 (TD)	Y. A. Tittle-Carroll Hardy	Detroit	10/30/55
2.	77	Y. A. Tittle-Hugh McElhenny	At New York	11/9/52
3.	77 (TD)	Y. A. Tittle-Billy Wilson	At Baltimore	12/2/56
4.	75 (TD)	Y. A. Tittle R. C. Owens	At Green Bay	10/11/59
5.	72 (TD)	Frank Albert-Sam Cathcart	At Cleveland (AAC)	10/30/49
	72 (TD)	Y. A. Tittle-Billy Wilson	Chic. Bears	10/23/55

Section III — Longest Plays   Pass Plays

6.	71		Y. A. Tittle-Hugh McElhenny	Los Angeles	10/4/53
7.	70		Y. A. Tittle-Joe Perry	At Detroit	11/14/54
8.	68	(TD)	Y. A. Tittle-Bill Jessup	Green Bay	12/5/54
9.	66		Frank Albert-John Strzykalski, lateraled to Len Eshmont	New York (AAC)	9/8/46
10.	64		Y. A. Tittle-Carroll Hardy	At Wash.	11/13/55
	64	(TD)	Y. A. Tittle-Joe Perry	At L.A.	11/9/58

LONGEST KICKOFF RETURNS

1.	105	(TD)	Abe Woodson	At Los Angeles	11/8/59
2.	96		Joe Arenas	Baltimore	12/16/56
3.	90	(TD)	Joe Arenas	Detroit	11/4/56
4.	87	(TD)	Joe Perry	At Brooklyn (AAC)	11/21/48
5.	82		Joe Arenas	Philadelphia	9/27/53
6.	65		Joe Arenas	At Detroit	10/11/53
	65		Bill Tidwell	At Detroit	11/14/54
7.	64		Joe Arenas	At Baltimore	11/24/57
	64		Joe Arenas	At Detroit	11/17/57
8.	62		Sam Cathcart	Detroit	10/22/50
9.	61		Joe Arenas	At Chicago Bears	10/18/53
	61		Dick Moegle	At Detroit	10/16/55

LONGEST PUNT RETURNS

1.	94	(TD)	Hugh McElhenny	At Chicago Bears	10/19/52
2.	67	(TD)	Joe Arenas	Baltimore	12/16/56
3.	65		Abe Woodson	Philadelphia	9/25/59
4.	62		Eddie Dove	Philadelphia	9/25/59
5.	57		Forrest Hall	At New York (AAC)	10/17/48
6.	55		Sam Cathcart	At Los Angeles (AAC)	11/13/49
7.	51		Sam Cathcart	Baltimore (AAC)	8/28/49
	51		Joe Arenas	Detroit	12/16/51
8.	50		Joe Arenas	At Baltimore	11/29/53
9.	38		Abe Woodson	Green Bay	12/7/58
10.	33		Jim Cason	At Detroit	10/8/50

LONGEST INTERCEPTION RETURNS

1.	90	(TD)	Ken Casanega (ran 68, lateraled to Ed Balatti, ran 22)	Chicago (AAC)	10/30/46
2.	66	(TD)	Lowell Wagner	New York (AAC)	11/27/49
3.	65	(TD)	Jim Cason	At Pittsburgh	10/14/51

4.	56		Ed Carr	Buffalo (AAC)	8/29/48
5.	54	(TD)	Bill Herchman	Chicago Bears	10/27/57
6.	52		Ned Mathews	Chicago (AAC)	10/12/47
7.	49		Ed Carr	At Chicago (AAC)	11/21/47
8.	47		Pete Brown	Green Bay	12/5/54
9.	44	(TD)	Rex Berry	At Detroit	10/16/55
	44		Abe Woodson	Green Bay	12/7/58

LONGEST FUMBLE RETURNS

1.	40	(TD)	Matt Hazeltine	At Detroit	10/18/59
2.	35	(TD)	Ed Carr	At Buffalo (AAC)	9/25/49
3.	24	(TD)	John Kuzman (AAC)	At Miami (AAC)	10/8/46
4.	20	(TD)	Len Eshmont	Buffalo (AAC)	11/2/46
	20		Jim Cason	Buffalo (AAC)	10/16/49
5.	17		Marv Matuszak	At New York	12/1/57

LONGEST PUNTS

1.	86	Larry Barnes	Chicago Cardinals	9/26/57
2.	82	Frank Albert	Buffalo (AAC)	8/29/48
3.	76	Larry Barnes	Baltimore	12/8/57
4.	75	Verl Lillywhite	Cleveland	9/30/51
5.	72	Frank Albert	New York (AAC)	11/27/49
6.	71	Tommy Davis	Chicago Bears	10/25/59

LONGEST FIELD GOALS

1.	47	Joe Vetrano	At Los Angeles (AAC)	12/5/48
2.	43	Tommy Davis	Philadelphia	9/25/59
3.	42	Gordy Soltau	Cleveland	9/30/51
	42	Tommy Davis	At Chicago Bears	11/15/59
4.	40	Gordy Soltau	Detroit	11/4/56
5.	39	Gordy Soltau	At Philadelphia	10/19/58
	39	Gordy Soltau	Los Angeles	10/17/56
	39	Gordy Soltau	Philadelphia	9/27/53

5000